OCR
Revise
Physics

A2

Exclusively endorsed by OCR for GCE Physics A

Second
Edition

David Sang

www.heinemann.co.uk

✓ Free online support
✓ Useful weblinks
✓ 24 hour online ordering

01865 888080

In Exclusive Partnership

Heinemann is an imprint of Pearson Education Limited, a company incorporated in England and Wales, having its registered office at Edinburgh Gate, Harlow, Essex, CM20 2JE. Registered company number: 872828

www.heinemann.co.uk

Heinemann is a registered trademark of Pearson Education Limited

Text © Pearson Education Limited 2008

First published 2001
This edition 2008

12 11 10 09 08
10 9 8 7 6 5 4 3 2 1

British Library Cataloguing in Publication Data
A catalogue record for this book is available from the British Library

ISBN 978 0 435583 75 0

Edited by Eileen Smith
Index compiled by Wendy Simpson
Designed by Wearset Ltd, Boldon, Tyne and Wear
Project managed and typeset by Wearset Ltd, Boldon, Tyne and Wear
Illustrated by Wearset Ltd, Boldon, Tyne and Wear
Cover photo from the Hubble Space Telescope of a dust shell around the star v838 Monoceratis © Science Photo Library/NASA/ESA/STSCI/H. Bond
Printed in China (GCC/01)
Every effort has been made to contact copyright holders of material reproduced in this book. Any omissions will be rectified in subsequent printings if notice is given to the publishers.

Contents

Introduction

How to use this revision guide

This revision guide is for the OCR GCE Physics A2 course. It is divided into two units to match Specification A. You may be taking a test at the end of each unit, or you may take all of the tests at the end of the course. The content is exactly the same.

Each unit begins with an **introduction** that summarises the content. It also reminds you of the topics from your GCSE and AS courses that the unit draws on.

The content of each unit is presented in **modules**, to help you divide your study into manageable chunks. Each module is dealt with in two or more spreads. These do the following:

- They **summarise** the content.
- They indicate **points to note**.
- They include **worked examples** of calculations.
- They include **diagrams** of the sort you might need to reproduce in tests.
- They provide **quick check** questions to help you test your understanding.

You can tackle the quick check questions as you work through the spread, or at the end of the spread. In the margin you will see markers to tell you at which point you have covered the necessary content to tackle each quick check question.

At the end of each unit, there are longer **end-of-unit questions** similar in style to those you will encounter in tests. **Answers** to all questions are provided at the end of the book.

You need to understand the **scheme of assessment** for your course. This is summarised on page v, opposite. At the end of the book, you will find a list of the **numerical data** and **formulae** that are provided in tests.

A note about units

In many of the worked examples, we have included units throughout the calculations. (See, for example, the worked examples on pages 4 and 5.) This can help to ensure that you end up with the correct units in your final answer.

In tests, it is not necessary to include units in intermediate steps in calculations, but make sure that your final numerical answers always include the correct units.

OCR A2 Physics – Assessment

There are three **units of assessment** (1, 2 and 3) in this A2 Physics course. These follow on from units 1, 2 and 3 of the AS Physics course. There are no optional units.

- Units 1 and 2 are externally assessed (by tests).
- Unit 3 includes assessment of **experimental skills** and is internally assessed.

As in the AS course, the units have different weightings (as shown in the table). Like the AS units, the A2 units that form the second half of the A level course have a combined weighting of 50% of the total A level.

Unit	OCR Code	Name	Duration of written test	Marks available	Weighting
1	G484	The Newtonian world	1 hour	60	15%
2	G485	Fields, particles and the frontiers of physics	1 hour 45 minutes	100	25%
3	G486	Practical skills in physics 2	internal assessment	40	10%

In Unit 3, practical tasks are set by OCR and marked within your centre, using a mark scheme provided by OCR.

Question types

There are no optional questions in the test papers – you have to answer all the questions.

- The questions are **structured questions** that require brief answers to several linked parts of a question.
- Parts of some questions require **extended answers**. These are used to assess the quality of your **written communication**.
- Some questions will involve a **synoptic** element. This means that they will draw on material you have studied in more than one unit, including AS units.
- Some questions have a **'stretch and challenge'** element. This means that there are fewer steps to guide you to the answer, putting more demand on your insight into the subject.

Use the mark allocation and the space available for your answer to guide how much you write.

About the tests

- **Written tests** will be available in January and June.
- **Practical tests** are only available in June.
- **Re-sits** may be taken as often as you wish; the best result counts, so you cannot end up with a lower score.
- **Aggregation** means combining the scores for each unit of assessment. To achieve an A-level grade at the end of the A2 course, you will have to carry your marks forward from the AS year.

A companion revision guide is available in this series for the AS part of the course.

> **Examiner tip**
>
> Unit 3 includes three tasks:
> - a qualitative task (10 marks)
> - a quantitative task (20 marks)
> - an evaluative task (10 marks)

UNIT 1

The Newtonian world

To help you organise your learning, each unit of the specification is broken down into modules. There are three modules in this unit.

Module 1: Newton's laws and momentum extends your understanding of the basic laws which describe how objects move. In particular, it defines the term *momentum* and shows how Newton's laws can be understood in terms of momentum. It also shows how problems involving interactions between objects (collisions and explosions) can be solved in terms of momentum.

Module 2: Circular motion and oscillations shows how the ideas of force, mass and acceleration can be applied in two important situations: when an object is moving around a circular path at a constant speed, and when an object is performing oscillations called *simple harmonic motion*. Although these situations are more complex than those considered earlier, they can still be understood in terms of the same basic ideas and equations.

Module 3: Thermal physics considers solids, liquids and gases. By thinking about the behaviour of particles (atoms and molecules) and applying the basic ideas of dynamics, we can explain the differences between the three states of matter. This module also looks at the macroscopic properties of materials, including the gas laws and specific heat capacity.

This unit counts for 30% of your A2 examination (15% of the total Advanced GCE qualification).

Your practical classes will have prepared you for the assessment of practical skills (Unit G486; see page v). There are some experiments that you must be able to describe as part of unit 1 (G484) for the examination. These are:

- a demonstration of Brownian motion (page 20), for which you should be able to describe and sketch the apparatus, summarise the method, describe the observations you would expect to make, and explain these observations
- an electrical determination of the specific heat capacity of a solid or liquid (page 25), for which you should be able to sketch the appropriate apparatus and label it, describe the measurements you would make, show how to calculate the result, and comment on possible sources of error and inaccuracy.

Module 1 – Newton's laws and momentum, pages 2–7

Topic (in this book)	Reference to specification	Ideas from GCSE and AS
Momentum	4.1.1 b–e, 4.1.2 a	Force and acceleration
Collisions and explosions	4.1.2 b–d	Vehicle safety
Newton's laws of motion	4.1.1 a, e–h	Newton's laws, $F = ma$

Module 2 – Circular motion and oscillations, pages 8–19

Topic (in this book)	Reference to specification	Ideas from GCSE and AS
Describing circular motion	4.2.1 a–e	Speed calculations
Centripetal force and acceleration	4.2.1 d–f	Force and acceleration
Gravitational fields	4.2.2 a–f	Acceleration due to gravity
Orbiting under gravity	4.2.2 g–n	Balanced and unbalanced forces
Simple harmonic motion	4.2.3 a–e, g–i	Wave properties, phase, etc.
More about SHM	4.2.3 f, j–n	

Module 3 – Thermal physics, pages 20–29

Topic (in this book)	Reference to specification	Ideas from GCSE and AS
Solid, liquid and gas	4.3.1 a–h	Kinetic model of matter
Temperature	4.3.2 a–e	Celsius scale
Specific heat capacity	4.3.3 a–d	Changes of state, thermal energy transfers
How gases behave	4.3.4 a–c	
Ideal gases	4.3.4 d–g	

End-of-unit questions, pages 30–33

Momentum

Key words

- linear momentum
- closed system
- elastic collision

Examiner tip

Linear momentum means momentum in a straight line. If an object is spinning, it also has *angular* momentum.

Examiner tip

See the note on units in calculations on page iv.

✓ *Quick check 1, 2 and 3*

In AS unit 1 (Mechanics), you saw how calculations involving changes between kinetic and potential energy can help to solve many problems. Another useful quantity in calculations is *momentum*.

Defining momentum

The **linear momentum** p of an object is the product of its mass m and its velocity v:

$$p = m \times v$$

An object has momentum *in a particular direction*. Hence momentum is a *vector* quantity. For example, the momentum of a woman of mass 60 kg running at 8 m s^{-1} due north is

$$p = m \times v = 60 \text{ kg} \times 8 \text{ m s}^{-1} = 480 \text{ kg m s}^{-1} \text{ due north}$$

The units of p are the units of m and v multiplied together: kg m s^{-1}. This can also be expressed as newton-seconds (N s). There is no special name for this unit.

Conservation of momentum

Like energy, momentum is a quantity that is *conserved*; that is, for any event, the (vector) total amount of momentum before the event equals the (vector) total afterwards. This principle of conservation is made use of in solving problems – see pages 4 and 5. Here are some examples of situations to illustrate this idea. In each case, it is important to identify the **closed system** (that is, the system with no external forces) for which momentum is conserved.

- One ball rolls along and strikes a second, identical ball. The first stops dead; the second moves off with the speed of the first one. The momentum of the first ball has been transferred to the second. Closed system = the two balls.

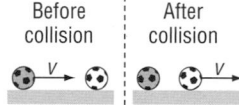

Before collision | After collision

- The car runs into a wall and stops dead. Where has its momentum gone? It has been transferred to the wall, and hence to the Earth, which moves *very* slightly faster to the right! Closed system = car + Earth.

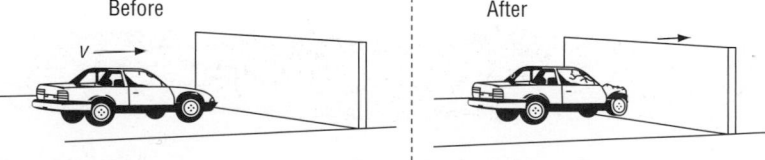

Before | After

- The ball falls towards the Earth, accelerating as it falls. It appears to be gaining momentum from nowhere. But the Earth is moving upwards, with a *very* small velocity. As the ball gains downward momentum, the Earth gains an equal and opposite upward momentum. The total momentum is zero. Closed system = ball + Earth.

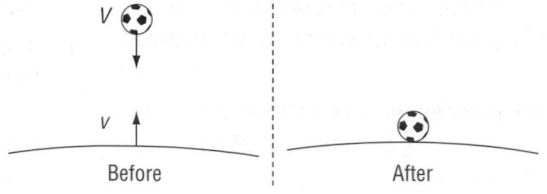

Before | After

The **principle of conservation of momentum** states that:

> When bodies interact, their total momentum is constant, provided no external force acts.

✓ *Quick check 4*

Momentum and kinetic energy

Both momentum (mv) and kinetic energy ($\frac{1}{2}mv^2$) depend on mass and velocity.

This makes it very difficult to have separate mental images of these quantities. It is important to recall that:

- Momentum is always conserved in a closed system.
- Kinetic energy is not always conserved.

Kinetic energy may be converted into other forms of energy, but momentum does not take different forms. A collision in which kinetic energy is conserved is described as elastic. **Elastic collisions** are springy – think back to the difference between elastic and plastic behaviour of materials in unit 1 of your AS course.

> **Hint**
>
> More about collisions on pages 4–5.

✓ *Quick check 5*

Momentum and force

It takes a *force* to change an object's momentum. The bigger the unbalanced or **net force**, the faster the change in momentum. This equation *defines* what is meant by force:

> **net force = rate of change of momentum**
> $$F = \Delta p / \Delta t$$

where F is the force in newtons, Δp the change in momentum in kg m s⁻¹ and Δt the change in time in seconds.

This is an alternative way of stating Newton's second law of motion. It is a better way, because it can apply to an object whose mass, as well as its velocity, is changing. In other words, $F = ma$ is a special case of Newton's second law for objects of constant mass.

> **Examiner tip**
>
> In this equation, the symbol Δ stands for 'change in' so that Δp means 'change in momentum'.

✓ *Quick check 6, 7 and 8*

QUICK CHECK QUESTIONS

1 Which of the following are *not* vector quantities: mass, velocity, momentum, kinetic energy?

2 A ship of mass 100 000 kg is sailing due west at 15 m s⁻¹. Calculate its momentum.

3 When a gun is fired, the bullet flies out very fast in a particular direction. The gun recoils more slowly in the opposite direction. Explain how momentum is conserved in this situation.

4 A car of mass 500 kg is travelling due north at 20 m s⁻¹. Some time later, it is travelling due south at 25 m s⁻¹. By how much has its momentum changed?

5 Who has more momentum, a boy of mass 40 kg running at 7.0 m s⁻¹ or a girl of mass 32 kg running at 8.0 m s⁻¹? Who has more kinetic energy?

6 In the equation $F = \Delta p / \Delta t$, what does Δt represent?

7 A car's momentum changes by 1200 kg m s⁻¹ in 4.0 s. What force acts on it to produce this change?

8 A stone of mass 0.4 kg is falling at 2.5 m s⁻¹. Half a second later, its downward velocity is 7.4 m s⁻¹. Calculate the stone's momentum at the start and finish of the 0.5 s interval. Use your answers to calculate the rate of change of its momentum, and hence the force acting on it.

Collisions and explosions

Collisions and explosions are examples of interactions between objects. In such situations momentum is conserved, and this can be used to solve problems. In *elastic* collisions, kinetic energy is also conserved; this can help in calculations.

Collisions

We will consider only **collisions** in one dimension (i.e. along a line), but we could apply the same ideas to solve problems in two or three dimensions. Since momentum is conserved, we can write:

momentum in any given direction before collision = momentum in that direction after collision

Key words

- collision
- explosion
- conservation of momentum
- elastic
- inelastic

Examiner tip

It is usually most helpful to start by drawing a pair of diagrams to show the situation before and after the interaction.

■ WORKED EXAMPLE

A trolley of mass 1 kg moving at 6 m s^{-1} collides with a second, stationary trolley of mass 2 kg. They stick together. With what velocity do they move off after the collision?

STEP 1 Draw a before-and-after diagram; mark on it all the available information.

Before ┊ After

$u_1 = 6$ m s^{-1} $u_2 = 0$ v

[1 kg]   [2 kg]   ┊   [1 kg][2 kg]

STEP 2 Using 'momentum before collision = momentum after collision' and substituting values gives

$$(1 \text{ kg} \times 6 \text{ m s}^{-1}) + (2 \text{ kg} \times 0 \text{ m s}^{-1}) = 3 \text{ kg} \times v$$

STEP 3 Solve this equation for v:

$$6 \text{ kg m s}^{-1} = 3 \text{ kg} \times v$$

$$v = 2 \text{ m s}^{-1}$$

The velocity is in the direction the first trolley had been moving. It may be intuitively obvious that, since the mass increases by a factor of 3, the velocity decreases to a third of its initial value.

Examiner tip

You could omit 2 kg × 0 m s^{-1}, since this is obviously zero.

✓ Quick check 1

■ WORKED EXAMPLE

Two trolleys, each of mass 1 kg and moving at 4 m s^{-1}, collide head-on. They bounce apart; each has velocity 2 m s^{-1} after the collision. Show that momentum is conserved. Is kinetic energy also conserved in this collision (is the collision elastic)?

STEP 1 Draw a before-and-after diagram; mark on it all the available information. Give velocities to the right as positive, and to the left as negative.

Before ┊ After

4 m s^{-1} −4 m s^{-1} ┊   −2 m s^{-1} 2 m s^{-1}

[1 kg]   [1 kg]   ┊   [1 kg]   [1 kg]

STEP 2 Here, we have to *show* that momentum is conserved. Calculate the momentum (*mv*) before and after collision *separately*:

momentum before = (1 kg × 4 m s⁻¹) + (1 kg × –4 m s⁻¹) = 0 kg m s⁻¹
momentum after = (1 kg × –2 m s⁻¹) + (1 kg × 2 m s⁻¹) = 0 kg m s⁻¹

Since momentum before collision = momentum after collision, we have shown that momentum is conserved.

STEP 3 Calculate the kinetic energy (½ *mv²*) for each trolley, before and after the collision. Mark these values on the diagram.

$$\text{kinetic energy before} = \left[\frac{1}{2} \times 1 \times 4^2\right] + \left[\frac{1}{2} \times 1 \times (-4)^2\right] = 8\,J + 8\,J = 16\,J$$

$$\text{kinetic energy after} = \left[\frac{1}{2} \times 1 \times (-2)^2\right] + \left[\frac{1}{2} \times 1 \times 2^2\right] = 2\,J + 2\,J = 4\,J$$

So most of the kinetic energy disappears in the collision. (The trolleys may be deformed; heat and sound are produced.) The collision is inelastic.

> **Examiner tip**
>
> Note that all values are positive, since squaring gets rid of the minus signs.

> ✓ *Quick check 2*

Explosions

Before an **explosion**, all parts of a system are at rest. Their combined momentum is zero. After the explosion, they are all flying apart. Each part has momentum, but their combined momentum *as a vector*, i.e. taking into account their different directions, is still zero.

■ WORKED EXAMPLE

Two spring-loaded trolleys of masses 5 kg and 3 kg are stationary. When the spring is released, they fly apart. The lighter trolley moves at 4 m s⁻¹. How fast does the heavier one move?

Before | After

5 kg 〰〰 3 kg | ← *v*   4 m s⁻¹ →
5 kg 〰〰〰〰   3 kg

STEP 1 Draw a before-and-after diagram; mark on it all the available information.
STEP 2 The total momentum after the spring is released is zero, so:
momentum of heavier trolley + momentum of lighter trolley = 0
STEP 3 Substitute values and solve for *v*:
(5 kg × *v*) + (3 kg × 4 m s⁻¹) = 0

$$v = \frac{-12\,\text{kg m s}^{-1}}{5\,\text{kg}} = -2.4\,\text{m s}^{-1}$$

The minus sign means that the heavier trolley is moving in the opposite direction to the lighter one, i.e. to the left.

> ✓ *Quick check 3*

QUICK CHECK QUESTIONS

1   A car of mass 500 kg travelling at 24 m s⁻¹ collides with a second, stationary car of mass 700 kg. The two cars move off together. What is their shared velocity?

2   A marble of mass 20 g is moving to the right at 4 m s⁻¹ when it collides with a smaller, stationary marble of mass 8 g. The smaller marble moves off at 5 m s⁻¹ to

the right. With what velocity (magnitude and direction) does the first marble move after the collision?

3   A cannon of mass 400 kg fires a shell of mass 20 kg. If the shell leaves the cannon at 300 m s⁻¹, with what velocity does the cannon recoil?

Newton's laws of motion

Key words

- Newton's laws
- impulse of a force

Hint

'Uniform motion' means constant velocity, i.e. constant speed in a straight line.

An unbalanced force causes an object's velocity to change – it makes it *accelerate*.

✓ *Quick check 1*

This section of Unit 1 has developed your understanding of forces and motion. You should now have a deeper understanding of **Newton's laws** of motion.

Newton's first law

> **An object continues in a state of rest or uniform motion in a straight line unless acted on by a net force.**

Newton's second law

This law extends the first law to say what happens when an unbalanced force acts on an object. The object accelerates; the greater the force, the greater the acceleration, so $F \propto a$. The acceleration also depends on the object's mass; the greater the mass, the smaller the acceleration produced by a given force. This gives $F \propto ma$, or $F = ma$ if we set the constant of proportionality to 1 (that is, we say $1\,\text{N} = 1\,\text{kg m s}^{-2}$). A better way to express Newton's second law is in terms of momentum (page 2):

> **When a net force acts on an object, the rate of change of momentum is equal to the force producing it, and takes place in the direction of the force.**

✓ *Quick check 2*

This statement is a definition of what is meant by a *force* – an interaction that causes a change in momentum. It is a more general statement of the second law than $F = ma$, because the object's mass may be changing, as well as its velocity.

Newton's third law

Two objects interacting with one another exert equal and opposite forces on each other, sometimes referred to as *action and reaction*. The two forces must:

- Be equal in magnitude but opposite in direction.
- Be of the same type (e.g. both contact forces, or gravitational, etc.).
- Act on different objects.

The third law applies for any two objects interacting with one another – they do not have to be in contact.

> **When two objects interact, the forces they exert on each other are equal in magnitude, but they act in opposite directions.**

✓ *Quick check 3*

This is related to the conservation of momentum. Object A exerts force F on object B. This causes B's momentum to change. At the same time, B exerts force $-F$ on A, so A's momentum changes. The two changes in momentum are equal in magnitude but opposite in direction, because the forces are equal and opposite. If A's momentum increases by a certain amount, B's must decrease by an equal amount. Momentum is conserved.

Impulse of a force

The greater the force and the longer the time for which it acts, the greater the change it will produce in the momentum of the object it is acting on. The quantity force × time is known as the **impulse of the force**.

impulse = change in momentum

For a force that varies with time, its impulse is equal to the area under the force-against-time graph.

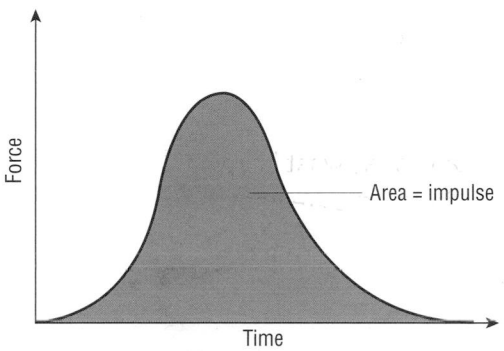

The equal and opposite forces described by Newton's third law act for equal times, so their impulses are equal and opposite. It follows that the objects have equal but opposite changes in momentum.

✓ *Quick check 4 and 5*

QUICK CHECK QUESTIONS

1 If an object is in equilibrium, what can you say about the resultant force acting on it? What can you say about its velocity?

2 A rocket rises steadily upwards at a constant speed of 500 m s^{-1}. Its initial mass is 5×10^4 kg; after 10 minutes, this has decreased to 4.4×10^4 kg. Calculate the average force acting on the rocket during this time. This force does work on the rocket. Explain how this changes the rocket's energy.

3 The diagram shows a person sitting still on a chair. Three forces are shown. Which pair must be equal in magnitude because of Newton's third law? Which pair must be equal because of Newton's second law?

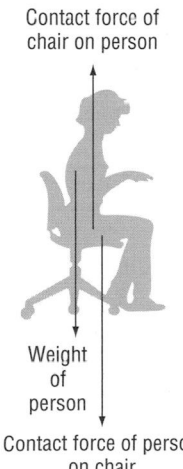

Contact force of chair on person

Weight of person

Contact force of person on chair

4 A force of 250 N acts on a car for 12 s. Calculate the impulse of the force. By how much does the momentum of the car change?

5 The graph shows how the force between two magnets changes. Determine the impulse of the force.

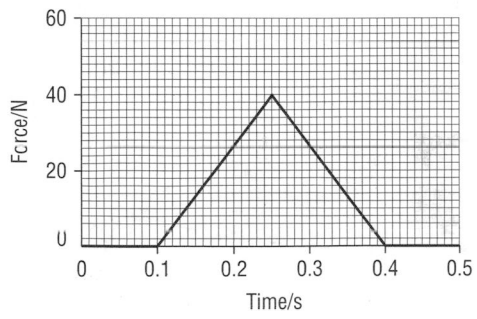

Hint

Use area of triangle
$= \frac{1}{2}$ base × height.

Describing circular motion

Key words

- radian
- centripetal force
- centripetal acceleration

Many objects move along paths that are circular (or nearly circular) – a stone whirled around on the end of a piece of string, the Earth in its orbit around the Sun, a car along a curved stretch of road, an aircraft changing direction, an electron orbiting the nucleus of an atom. Since an object moving along a curved path is not moving in a straight line, it is an example of a moving object that is not in equilibrium.

Angular displacement; angles in radians

As an object moves along a circular path, it can be useful to state its position in terms of the angle θ through which it has moved relative to its starting position. This is called its *angular displacement* and is often given in **radians** rather than degrees. One radian is the angle subtended by the arc of a circle of length equal to its radius. The abbreviation for radians is **rad**.

The angle θ depends on the radius r of the circle and the length of the arc s. In radians,

$$\theta = \frac{s}{r} \text{ or } s = r\theta$$

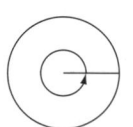

For an angle of 1 rad, the length of the arc is equal to the radius:

$$\theta = \frac{r}{r} = 1$$

$\theta = 1$ rad

For a whole circle, the arc $s = 2\pi r$. Hence,

$$\theta = 2\pi\frac{r}{r} = 2\pi.$$

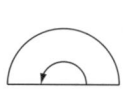 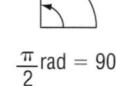

2π rad $= 360°$ π rad $= 180°$ $\frac{\pi}{2}$ rad $= 90°$

- To convert from degrees to radians: multiply by $\pi/180°$.
- To convert from radians to degrees: multiply by $180°/\pi$.

■ WORKED EXAMPLE

A car travels one-eighth of the way around a circular track. Through what angle θ has it moved in degrees, and in radians?

STEP 1 Since a full circle is 360°, we can calculate the angle in degrees:

$$\theta = \frac{360°}{8} = 45°$$

STEP 2 Convert to radians:

$$\theta = 45 \times \frac{\pi}{180} \text{ rad} = \frac{\pi}{4} \text{ rad} = 0.79 \text{ rad}$$

✓ *Quick check 1, 2 and 3*

Speed around a circular path

To calculate the speed of an object moving in a circular path, we need to know a distance and a time. For example:

$$\text{speed} = \frac{\text{circumference of circle}}{\text{time to complete one trip around circle}}$$

Since the circumference of a circle of radius r is $2\pi r$, if the time to complete one circuit is t we have

$$v = \frac{2\pi r}{t}$$

✓ *Quick check 4*

Constant speed, changing velocity

When an object moves in a circular path, its velocity is at a tangent to the circle. If it is moving at an unchanging speed, its *speed* is constant but its *velocity* is changing, because its direction of movement is changing.

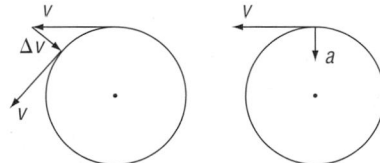

The small arrow, Δv, shows how the velocity vector changes from one position to the next. This arrow indicates the direction of the change in velocity, and hence the direction of the acceleration. It is directed towards the centre of the circle, and its magnitude is constant.

To produce this acceleration, there must be an unbalanced force of constant magnitude always acting perpendicular to the motion, that is, towards the centre of the circle. Hence the forces acting on an object with circular motion are unbalanced; it is not in equilibrium.

So, for uniform motion in a circle:

- the object moves at a constant speed
- it has an acceleration towards the centre of the circle
- the acceleration is caused by a net force directed towards the centre of the circle.

The adjective that describes anything directed towards the centre of a circle is **centripetal**. Hence an object moving at a steady speed in a circular path has a **centripetal acceleration** caused by a **centripetal force**. The origins of centripetal forces are discussed on the next page.

✔*Quick check 5*

QUICK CHECK QUESTIONS

1 Convert the following angles in degrees to radians: 360°; 180°; 90°; 60°; 45°.

2 Convert the following angles in radians to degrees: 1.0 rad; 0.25 rad; π rad; 2π rad; $\pi/5$ rad.

3 Which is greater, 2.0 rad or 120°?

4 An aircraft is circling, waiting to land at an airport. Its circular path has a diameter of 20 km, and its speed is 120 m s^{-1}.
   (a) How long will it take to complete one circuit of its path?
   (b) In what time interval will the direction in which it is travelling change by 30°?

5 A toy train runs at a steady speed around a circular track. Which of the following are changing as it moves: its distance from the centre of the circle; its speed; its velocity; its centripetal acceleration; the centripetal force acting on it? Explain your answers.

Centripetal force and acceleration

Key words

- centripetal force
- centripetal acceleration

A **centripetal force** is needed to keep an object moving along a circular path. Without such a force, the object would fly off in a straight line, at a tangent to the circle.

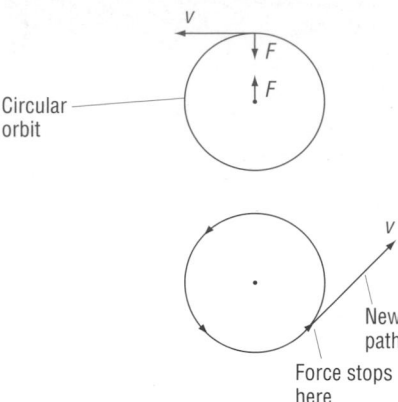

Origins of centripetal forces

Take care! The word centripetal describes the direction of the force (towards the centre), but it does not tell you how the force arises. A centripetal force may arise in a variety of ways. Here are some examples.

A stone is whirled around on the end of a string.	The tension in the string pulls the stone towards the centre of the circle.
A plane banks to follow a curved path.	The horizontal component of the lift force pushes the plane towards the centre of the circle.
A satellite orbits the Earth.	The Earth's gravitational pull on the satellite is directed towards the centre of the Earth.
An electron orbits the nucleus of an atom.	The electrostatic attraction of the nucleus pulls the electron towards it.

✓*Quick check 1*

The size of the force

In each case, the moving object is pushed by the force towards the centre of the circle, but it never gets any closer. The force must be just large enough; any smaller, and the object will move away outwards; any bigger, and it will move inwards.

The centripetal force needed to make an object follow a curved path depends on three factors.

- The object's mass m: the greater the mass, the greater the force needed.
- The object's speed v: the greater the speed, the greater the force needed.
- The radius r of the path: the smaller the radius, the tighter the curve and the greater the force needed.

These quantities are combined in the following equation for F:

$$\text{centripetal force } F = \frac{mv^2}{r}$$

■ WORKED EXAMPLE

A light aircraft of mass 500 kg is moving at a steady speed of 120 m s⁻¹ along a curved path of radius 2 km. What centripetal force is needed to keep it on this path?

Substitute values in the equation for *F*, and solve:

$$F = \frac{mv^2}{r} = \frac{500 \text{ kg} \times (120 \text{ m s}^{-1})^2}{2000 \text{ m}} = 3600 \text{ N}$$

✓ *Quick check 2 and 3*

Calculating centripetal acceleration

Since acceleration *a* = *F*/*m*, we have

$$a = \frac{v^2}{r}$$

(Strictly speaking, it is more correct to start from *a* = *v²*/*r* and use *F* = *ma* to deduce that *F* = *mv²*/*r*.)

■ WORKED EXAMPLE

A spacecraft orbits above the Earth's surface at a height of 200 km. Its speed is 8 km s⁻¹. Calculate its centripetal acceleration. (Radius of Earth = 6400 km.)

STEP 1 Calculate the radius of the orbit:
radius of orbit *r* = (6400 + 200) km = 6600 km
STEP 2 Calculate the centripetal acceleration (note that kilometres must be converted to metres throughout):

$$\text{centripetal acceleration } a = \frac{v^2}{r} = \frac{(8000 \text{ m s}^{-1})^2}{6.6 \times 10^6 \text{ m}} = 9.7 \text{ m s}^{-2}$$

Examiner tip

Note that the answer is slightly less than the value of *g* at the Earth's surface, because the satellite is slightly further away from the centre of the Earth.

✓ *Quick check 4 and 5*

QUICK CHECK QUESTIONS

1   When a car follows a curved route, what force provides the necessary centripetal force?

2   A stone of mass 0.5 kg is whirled round at the end of a piece of string 40 cm in length. If it completes two complete revolutions in 1.0 s, what is the tension in the string?

Examiner tip

Think back to your study of the forces on vehicles in Module 1.

Examiner tip

First calculate the stone's speed.

3   A centripetal force is needed to make a car go round a bend. Use the equation *F* = *mv²*/*r* to explain why a bigger force is needed for a given speed when the car is following a more sharply curved bend.

4   Calculate the centripetal acceleration of a car which, travelling at 25 m s⁻¹, goes around a bend of radius 50 m.

5   The gravitational acceleration near the Moon's surface is 1.6 m s⁻². Calculate the speed of a satellite orbiting the Moon close to its surface. (Radius of orbit = 1800 km.)

Gravitational fields

Key words

- gravitational field strength
- weight
- field lines
- universal gravitational constant

The Earth has a *gravitational field*. This means that, if an object with mass is placed anywhere in that field, it will feel a force – the pull of the Earth's gravity. This force has another name – the *weight* of the object. A gravitational field is a field of force, created by any object with mass.

Representing a field

Field lines (lines of force) represent a gravitational field.

- The arrows show the direction of the force on a mass placed in the field.
- Lines closer together represent a stronger field.

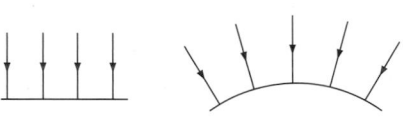
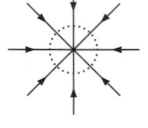

Near the Earth's surface, the field is uniform. The field lines are effectively parallel; the force on an object is the same at all positions in the field.

On a larger scale, the Earth has a spherical field. The field lines diverge; the field gets weaker the further we move away from the surface.

For a uniform sphere, the external field is the same as if all of its mass were concentrated at the centre.

✓*Quick check 1*

Defining field strength

The **gravitational field strength** g at a point in a field is the force per unit mass that acts on an object placed at that point.

Since force per unit mass is F/m, we can write

$$g = \frac{F}{m} \quad \text{or} \quad F = mg$$

You should recognise this as the equation used to calculate the weight of an object of mass m.

Examiner tip

The force that makes an object fall is gravity. Comparing $F = mg$ with $F = ma$ shows that $a = g$.

On the surface of the Earth, g has the approximate value

$$g = 9.81 \text{ N kg}^{-1}$$

This varies only slightly over the surface of the Earth.

✓*Quick check 2*

Note that this value is the same as that of the acceleration of free fall, 9.81 m s^{-2}.

Newton's law of gravitation

Newton's law tells us how to calculate the gravitational force F between two objects of masses M and m separated by a distance r:

$$F = -\frac{GMm}{r^2}$$

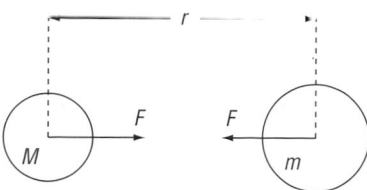

Here $G = -6.67 \times 10^{-11}$ N m^2 kg^{-2} is the **universal gravitational constant.**

This is an example of an *inverse square law*: F is proportional to $1/r^2$.

The objects are *point masses*, as if all of an object's mass is concentrated at its centre of gravity. Each of the two objects feels the same force (even if their masses are different), but in opposite directions. They are an equal and opposite pair of forces, as described by Newton's third law of motion (page 6).

Hint

Centre of gravity – see AS Unit 1, page 19.

Hint

For another inverse square law, see page 38.

g for a point mass

For a point mass M, the gravitational field strength g at a distance r is

$$g = -\frac{GM}{r^2}$$

The minus sign simply shows that the force is attractive.

■ **WORKED EXAMPLE**

Find the mass of the Earth, given that $g = -9.81$ N kg^{-1} at its surface. (Radius of the Earth $= 6.4 \times 10^6$ m, $G = -6.67 \times 10^{-11}$ N m^2 kg^{-2}.)

STEP 1 Rearrange the equation $g = -GM/r^2$:

$$M = -\frac{gr^2}{G}$$

STEP 2 Substitute values for g, r and G, and calculate the result:

$$M = \frac{9.8 \text{ N kg}^{-1} \times (6.4 \times 10^6 \text{ m})^2}{6.67 \times 10^{-11} \text{ N m}^2 \text{ kg}^{-2}} = 6.0 \times 10^{24} \text{ kg}$$

✔ *Quick check 3*

QUICK CHECK QUESTIONS

1 Draw diagrams including field lines to explain the following. When you go upstairs, your weight is effectively unchanged; if you climb Mount Everest, your weight decreases very slightly; if you are in a spacecraft 200 km above the Earth's surface, your weight is significantly less than on the surface.

2 The Moon's gravitational field strength is 1.6 N kg^{-1}. Calculate the weight of a 5 kg rock on the Moon. If dropped, how far will it fall in 1 s?

3 Two asteroids, of masses 4×10^{10} kg and 8×10^{10} kg, are separated by 20 km in space. Calculate the gravitational force each exerts on the other. Draw a diagram to show the directions of these forces.

Orbiting under gravity

Key words

- Kepler's third law
- geostationary orbit

The motion of planets around the Sun and of satellites around planets can be analysed by combining our knowledge of circular motion with knowledge of gravitational fields. We assume that planets move in circular orbits, although in reality their orbits are slightly elliptical. Planets are themselves natural satellites of the Sun.

Equations for planetary and satellite motion

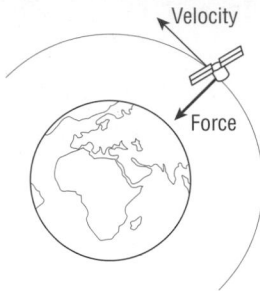

A centripetal force acts on a satellite to keep it moving in a circle. The only force acting on the satellite is the force of the Earth's gravity, so this must provide the centripetal force. We can thus equate expressions for gravitational and centripetal forces:

$$\frac{mv^2}{r} = \frac{GMm}{r^2}$$

r and m cancel, leaving

$$v^2 = \frac{GM}{r}$$

We can also relate the speed v to the period T and radius r of orbit:

$$v = \text{distance/time} = 2\pi r/T$$

Hint

T is the period of orbit – the time taken for the planet or satellite to make one complete orbit, a distance of $2\pi r$.

Kepler's third law $T^2 \propto r^3$

This law relates the period T of a planet to the radius r of its orbit. To derive the law, we must use the third equation above ($v = 2\pi r/T$) to eliminate v from the second equation.

$$v^2 = \frac{GM}{r}$$

Substituting for v gives:

$$\left(\frac{2\pi r}{T}\right)^2 = \frac{GM}{r}$$

Squaring and rearranging gives:

$$T^2 = \left(\frac{4\pi^2}{GM}\right) r^3$$

Examiner tip

You need to be able to deduce the equation $T^2 = (4\pi^2/GM)r^3$ from first principles, i.e. as shown on this page.

✓ *Quick check 1*

Kepler used measurements of the planets to show that T^2 is proportional to r^3; this is his third law.

Geostationary orbits

A satellite in a **geostationary orbit** will always remain in the same place above the equator. Seen from a point on the Earth's surface, they are always at the same point in the sky. This means that they can be used for relaying TV, telephone and other telecommunications signals from one place on the Earth's surface to another. The satellite must:

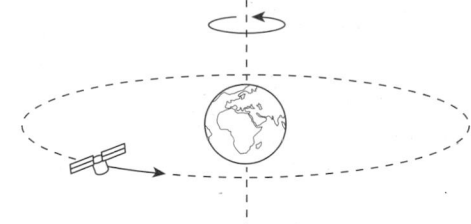

- have a period(the time taken to complete an orbit) of 24 h;

- be in orbit above the equator;

- move in the same direction as the rotation of the Earth.

■ WORKED EXAMPLE

Calculate the height above the Earth's surface (altitude) for a satellite to be in geostationary orbit.

$G = 6.67 \times 10^{-11}$ N m² kg⁻²; mass of Earth $M = 6.0 \times 10^{24}$ kg; radius of Earth = 6400 km.

STEP 1 Combine the formulae $v^2 = GM/r$ and $v = 2\pi r/T$:

$$\frac{4\pi^2 r^2}{T^2} = \frac{GM}{r}$$

STEP 2 Rearrange this equation:

$$r^3 = \frac{GMT^2}{4\pi^2}$$

STEP 3 Substitute values for G, M and T (= 24 h = 86 400 s):
$$r^3 = 6.7 \times 10^{-11} \times 6.0 \times 10^{24} \times 86\,400^2/4\pi^2$$

STEP 4 Work out the result on your calculator. Take care: there are a lot of functions here! Pressing the right buttons gives $r = 42.4 \times 10^6$ m.

STEP 5 Take away the radius of the Earth:
altitude = (42.4 × 10⁶ m − 6.4 × 10⁶ m) = 36 × 10⁶ m or 36 000 km

> **Examiner tip**
>
> This calculation follows the same approach as the derivation of Kepler's third law.

> **Examiner tip**
>
> Get as far as possible using algebra before substituting any of the numbers.

✓ *Quick check 2, 3 and 4*

QUICK CHECK QUESTIONS

Take $G = 6.67 \times 10^{-11}$ N m² kg⁻²; mass of Earth $M = 6.0 \times 10^{24}$ kg; radius of Earth = 6400 km.

1 Mars orbits the Sun at a greater distance than the Earth. What can you say about the period of its orbit, compared with the Earth's? And its orbital speed, compared with the Earth's?

2 The period of the Moon around the Earth is 27.3 days.
  (a) Calculate the number of seconds in 28 days.
  (b) Calculate the radius of the Moon's orbit around the Earth.

> **Examiner tip**
>
> Start with Step 1 in the worked example.

3 A satellite is put into orbit 600 km above the Earth. Calculate its speed in m s⁻¹ and its period.

4 The mass of Mars is 6.42×10^{23} kg and its radius is 3.38×10^6 m. A satellite with a period of 120 minutes is placed in orbit around Mars. Calculate its height above the surface of Mars.

Simple harmonic motion

Key words

- displacement
- amplitude
- period
- frequency
- angular frequency

Examiner tip

Forced oscillations are covered on page 19.

Start a pendulum swinging; pluck a stretched string; pull and release a mass on a spring. All of these result in **free oscillations**, in which a mass vibrates freely at its natural frequency. In many situations, these oscillations take the form of what is called **simple harmonic motion (SHM).**

Defining terms

An oscillation can be represented by a displacement–time graph, just like a wave. The following terms have the same meanings as for a wave:

- **displacement** x: distance of the mass from its equilibrium position (metres)

- **amplitude** A: greatest value of the displacement (metres)

- **period** T: time for one complete oscillation (seconds)

- **frequency** f: number of oscillations per second (hertz, Hz)

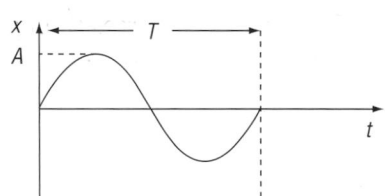
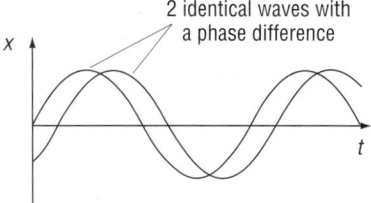

Frequency and period are related by

$$f = \frac{1}{T} \text{ or } T = \frac{1}{f}$$

We define a further quantity: **angular frequency** ω. We consider one complete oscillation or cycle as 2π radians. Then the angular frequency is the number of oscillations per second, measured in radians. It follows that

$$\omega = 2\pi f$$

Oscillations with the same frequency that reach their maximum displacements simultaneously are said to be **in phase** with one another. Oscillations with the same frequency that reach their maximum displacements at different times are said to be **out of phase** with one another. The **phase difference** between two such oscillations is given as a fraction of a cycle (2π radians).

$$\frac{1}{2} \text{ cycle phase difference} = \pi \text{ rad}$$

$$\frac{1}{4} \text{ cycle phase difference} = \pi/2 \text{ rad}$$

✓*Quick check 1 and 2*

Defining SHM

Not all oscillations are simple harmonic. For SHM, a mass is displaced from a central position, where it is in equilibrium. A restoring force F acts in the opposite direction to the displacement x; for SHM, this force must be proportional to x. This gives the mass an acceleration a, back towards the central position, that is proportional to x. Hence:

Simple harmonic motion occurs when the acceleration of a mass is directed towards a fixed point and is proportional to its displacement from that point.

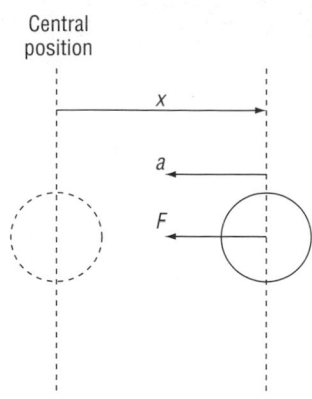

Central position

We can write this as an equation that involves the frequency f:

$$a = -\omega^2 x \text{ or } a = -(2\pi f)^2 x$$

An important characteristic of SHM is that the period (or frequency) is independent of the amplitude.

✓ *Quick check 3*

Back and forth

The mass speeds up as it approaches the midpoint. As soon as it passes through the midpoint, it starts to decelerate. Its maximum speed is at the midpoint:

$$v_{max} = 2\pi f A$$

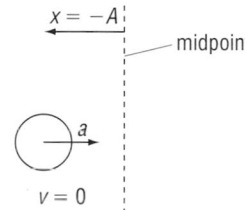

$x = -A$ — midpoint

$v = 0$

Here, the restoring force $F = ma$ has its greatest value. The mass is instantaneously at rest.
displacement $x = -A$
velocity $v = 0$
acceleration a = maximum

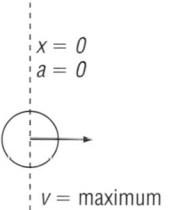

$x = 0$
$a = 0$

v = maximum

At the midpoint, the mass is moving fastest, although there is no force on it. It is in equilibrium ($F = ma = 0$).
displacement $x = 0$
velocity v = maximum
acceleration $a = 0$

$x = +A$

a

$v = 0$

Here, the mass's velocity is again zero, but the restoring force again has its maximum value.
displacement $x = +A$
velocity $v = 0$
acceleration a = maximum

✓ *Quick check 4 and 5*

QUICK CHECK QUESTIONS

1   For the oscillation represented by the graph, what are the values of: amplitude, period, frequency, angular frequency?

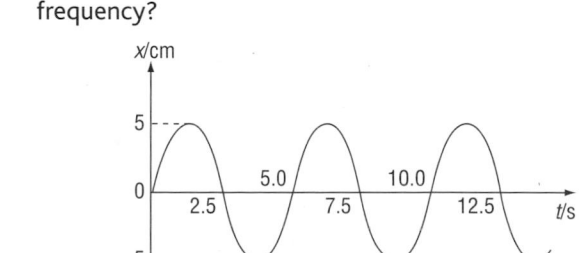

2   The swings of a pendulum are timed. It completes 20 swings in 17.4 s. What are its period, frequency and angular frequency?

3   A mass is vibrating on the end of a spring. Its acceleration a (in m s^{-2}) is related to its displacement x (in m) from a fixed point by $a = -(40\pi)^2 x$. What are its angular frequency and its frequency? What is the period of its oscillation?

4   A pendulum swings from side to side. At what point in its oscillation is its speed greatest? At what point is its acceleration greatest?

5   A mass between two springs moves with SHM. It oscillates between two points 5.0 cm apart, and completes 40 oscillations in 1 minute. What is its maximum speed?

Examiner tip

First calculate the amplitude and frequency of the mass.

More about SHM

Examiner tip

Recall that the acceleration is in the opposite direction to the displacement.

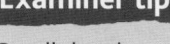 **Quick check 1**

We can think of oscillations that are simple harmonic as being 'pure' oscillations. They give an x–t graph that is a sine curve.

SHM graphs

The velocity–time graph is the gradient of the displacement–time graph.

- At the start of the x–t graph, the gradient is steep and positive, so the velocity is high and positive.
- When the x–t graph reaches a maximum, its gradient is zero so $v = 0$.

The a–t graph is the gradient of the v–t graph. It has troughs where the x–t graph has peaks.

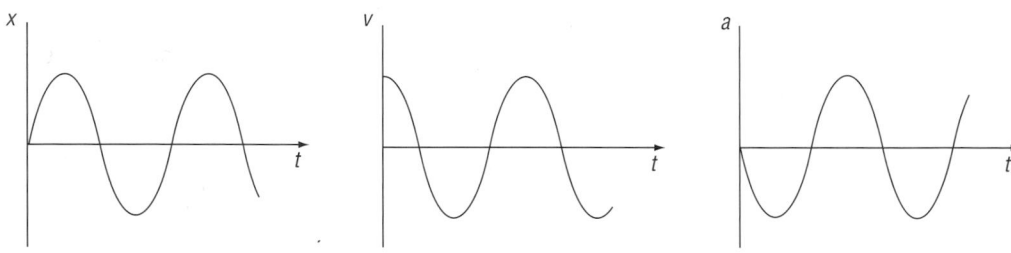

SHM equations

The information contained in a displacement–time graph can also be represented by an equation:

$$x = A \sin (2\pi ft) \quad \text{or} \quad x = A \cos (2\pi ft)$$

The difference between these equations is this:

- If the oscillation starts ($t = 0$) at the midpoint ($x = 0$), use the sine version (because $\sin 0 = 0$).
- If the oscillation starts ($t = 0$) at the endpoint ($x = A$), use the cosine version (because $\cos 0 = 1$).

Take care! When using these equations, ensure that your calculator is working in radians, not degrees!

Quick check 2 and 3

Energy changes

The energy of the oscillating mass is transformed back and forth between kinetic and potential forms as it oscillates.

- Midpoint: maximum velocity, therefore maximum kinetic energy and zero gravitational potential energy.
- Endpoints: zero velocity, therefore zero kinetic energy and maximum gravitational potential energy.

Quick check 4

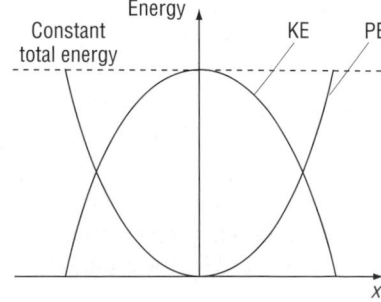

Damping

If the oscillating mass loses no energy, it will oscillate for ever with the same amplitude.

However, if it loses energy, we say the oscillations are *damped*. Their amplitude decreases.

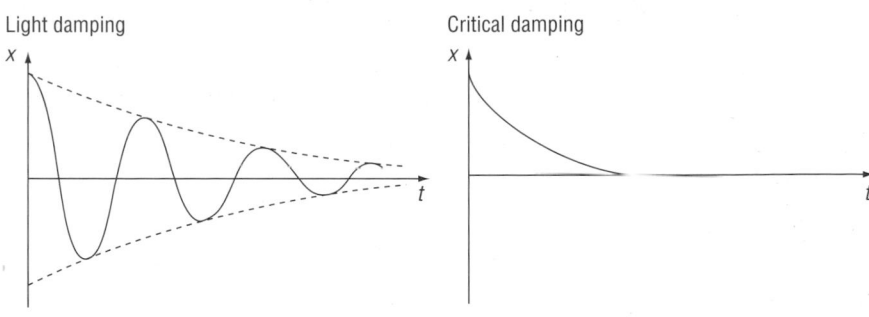

Light damping

Critical damping

- Light damping: the amplitude decreases gradually as the mass oscillates.

- Critical damping: the damping is heavy enough for the displacement just to decrease to zero (the equilibrium position) without oscillation. With a little less damping, the mass overshoots the midpoint.

Damping is caused by frictional forces, e.g. drag of the air, or viscous drag in oil. A car suspension system is usually critically damped, so that the passengers do not bounce up and down each time the car passes over a bump in the road.

Resonance

It may be possible to force a mass to oscillate at any frequency. This is called a **forced oscillation**. If the forcing frequency matches the natural frequency of free oscillations, the amplitude increases to a large value. This is **resonance**.

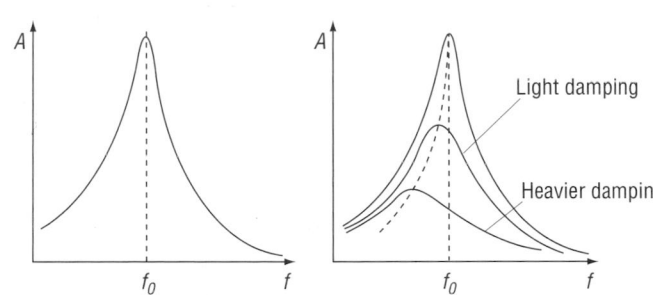

Light damping

Heavier damping

The graph shows that:

- At frequencies slightly above and below resonance, the amplitude is less.

- Damping reduces the amplitude at resonance, and tends to shift the resonant frequency.

Resonance can be useful, e.g. in tuning a radio (the resonant frequency of the tuning circuit is adjusted to match the frequency of the signal) or a problem, e.g. when suspension bridges shake or when vibrations of an earthquake build up, shaking buildings apart.

✓*Quick check 5*

QUICK CHECK QUESTIONS

1 The graph shows one oscillation for a vibrating mass. Copy the graph, and beneath it sketch the corresponding velocity–time and acceleration–time graphs.

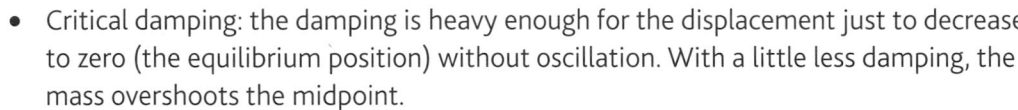

2 A mass oscillates such that its displacement x in cm is represented by the equation

$$x = 4 \cos(0.6t)$$

What are the values of the amplitude and frequency of this motion? What is the value of x when $t = 5$ s?

3 Write an x–t equation for oscillations of amplitude 0.2 m and frequency 0.5 Hz, for a mass whose initial displacement is zero. Calculate its displacement when $t = 0.2$ s.

4 Look at the energy graph opposite. When the mass is halfway between the midpoint and the endpoint of its oscillation, which is greater, its kinetic energy or its potential energy?

5 Look at the resonance graph above. What happens to the sharpness of the resonance curve as damping increases?

Solid, liquid and gas

Hint

'Particles' here can refer to atoms, molecules or ions.

In the kinetic model of matter, we relate the properties of matter to the behaviour of the particles of which it is made. solids, liquids and gases differ in the spacing, ordering and motion of their particles.

Molecules in solids, liquids and gases

A vibrating particle in a solid has a mixture of kinetic and potential energy. Its energy switches back and forth between kinetic and potential energy as it vibrates.

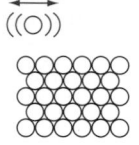 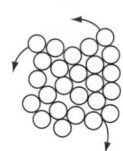 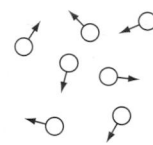

In a solid, the molecules vibrate about fixed positions, being bonded to their neighbours.

In a liquid, the molecules can move more freely. They are more weakly bonded with their neighbours.

In a gas, molecules can move freely and rapidly. They are not bonded to one another.

A particle moving about in a liquid or gas has **translational kinetic energy** (translational means 'moving from place to place'). It also has potential energy, because it has been separated from its former neighbours.

✔ *Quick check 1*

Brownian motion

Examiner tip

You should be able to describe an experiment to demonstrate Brownian motion and discuss its interpretation in terms of molecular motion.

When smoke particles are observed in still air, they are seen to move about in a jerky, random way. They are being buffeted by the (invisible) molecules of the air which are moving about at high speed.

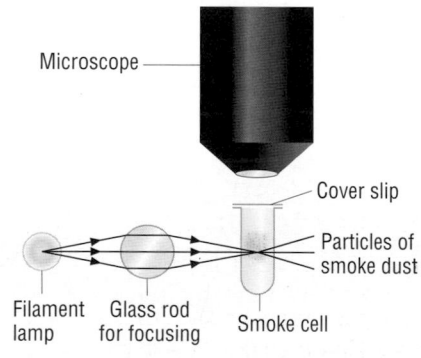

Microscope

Cover slip

Particles of smoke dust

Filament lamp   Glass rod for focusing   Smoke cell

Equipment for observing Brownian motion

Examiner tip

You should recall that pressure is measured in pascals; $1 \text{ Pa} = 1 \text{ N m}^{-2}$.

✔ *Quick check 2*

Pressure

Fluids (liquids and gases) exert pressure because their moving particles collide with the walls of their container. As they bounce off the walls, they exert a force (their momentum changes). Pressure is defined as follows:

pressure = force/area $p = F/A$

Internal energy

What happens when a substance is heated? Energy is transferred to the substance. This increases its **internal energy**. We can understand internal energy in terms of the energy of the particles that make up the substance.

The internal energy of an object depends on 'the state of the system' – its temperature, pressure, volume, etc. It is simply the sum of the energies (kinetic and potential) of the particles making up the object. The energy of each particle keeps changing in a random fashion, due to collisions with neighbours, but if we could take a snapshot of the system at an instant in time and add up the energies of all the particles, we would find the internal energy. More formally:

> **The internal energy of a system is the sum of a random distribution of kinetic and potential energies associated with the particles of the system.**

Energy can be transferred to a system in many ways: by heating, by doing work, electrically, etc. The energy transferred is shared among the molecules of the system, increasing their energies. This increases the internal energy of the system.

✓*Quick check 3 and 4*

Changes of state

Energy must be supplied to melt a solid, or to boil a liquid. As it *changes state*, the substance remains at a steady temperature. The energy input is increasing the potential energy of the molecules, not their kinetic energy. (Bonds are broken between molecules, but they do not move any faster.)

- In **melting**, a solid becomes a liquid at a fixed temperature (the melting point). The molecules' potential energy increases, but their average kinetic energy does not.

- Similarly, in **boiling**, molecular potential energy increases, but kinetic energy is constant.

- In **evaporation**, a liquid turns to a gas at a temperature below the boiling point. Only the more energetic molecules escape from the liquid, so the mean kinetic energy of those remaining in the liquid decreases; its temperature drops.

✓*Quick check 5*

QUICK CHECK QUESTIONS

1 In which state (solid, liquid or gas) do the molecules of a substance have the greatest kinetic energy? In which state the greatest potential energy?

2 Calculate the pressure of a gas (in Pa) if it exerts a force of 80 kN on an area of 0.20 m².

3 A block of ice is cut exactly in half. What can you say about the internal energy of each half, compared to that of the original block?

4 Which of the following energy transfers will increase the internal energy of a block of ice? (Assume no other transfers take place.)
   - carrying it upstairs
   - heating it with an electrical heater
   - putting it in a fast-moving aircraft.

5 The graph shows the results of an experiment in which a material, initially solid, is heated at a steady rate. Its temperature changes as shown.
State whether the material is solid, liquid or gas at points A–E.
At which of points A–E is its internal energy increasing?

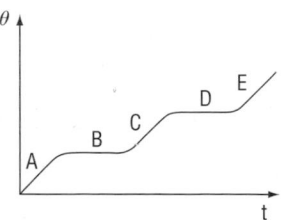

Temperature

Key words

- thermal equilibrium
- Kelvin scale
- thermodynamic scale

When two objects are at different temperatures, energy is transferred from the hotter object to the colder one. This may seem like an obvious statement, but it tells us what it means to say that objects are at different temperatures.

Thermal energy

When energy is transferred because of a temperature difference, it is described as **thermal energy**. It doesn't matter what the *mechanism* of transfer is – it could be conduction, convection or radiation. The important thing is that a temperature difference is the cause of the transfer.

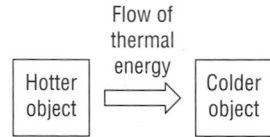

Thermal equilibrium

If two objects or regions are at the same temperature, no thermal energy will be transferred between them. We say that they are in **thermal equilibrium**. Although there is no *net* transfer of energy, energy is passing back and forth between them all the time, but at equal rates in the two directions.

✓ *Quick check 1 and 2*

Absolute zero

As a substance is cooled, its particles move more and more slowly. At a temperature called **absolute zero** (–273.15 °C), its particles would reach their lowest possible energy. In practice, this temperature is unattainable. At absolute zero, all substances would have a minimum internal energy.

✓ *Quick check 3*

Temperature scales

The **Celsius scale** of temperature was devised to give 100 degrees between the melting point of water (0 °C) and its boiling point (100 °C). Temperatures in °C below the melting point of water are therefore *negative*.

The Celsius scale is a practical scale of measurement; it is easy to obtain melting ice and boiling water in order to calibrate a thermometer. However, it is preferable to define a scale of temperature which does not depend on the properties of a specific material.

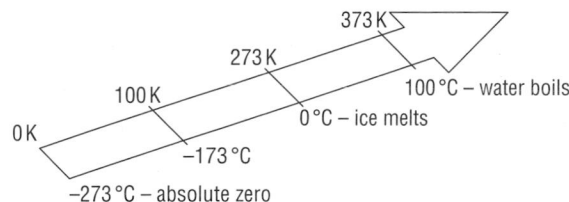

A more useful temperature scale in the study of the behaviour of matter is the **thermodynamic scale** or **Kelvin scale**. This scale has a fixed starting point: absolute zero. This is written as 0 kelvin or 0 K, and temperatures, often called *absolute temperatures* or *thermodynamic temperatures*, are expressed as 10 K, 200 K, etc. (note: 'kelvin', *not* 'degrees kelvin').

The unit interval on this scale, known as 1 kelvin (1 K), is also fixed – it is an SI base unit. So the thermodynamic scale does not depend on the physical properties of any particular substance. A *temperature rise* of 1 K (again, *not* 'degree kelvin') is identical with a rise of 1 °C.

Absolute zero, 0 K, equals –273.15 °C (though the approximation 273 is often acceptable). To convert a temperature from one scale to the other:

°C = K – 273.15
K = °C + 273.15

The symbols are *t* for temperatures in °C and *T* for temperatures in K. Hence:

T/K = t/°C + 273.15

QUICK CHECK QUESTIONS

Object	Temperature/°C
A	400
B	470
C	390
D	400

1   The table shows the temperatures of four objects.
    (a) Which two are in thermal equilibrium?
    (b) In which direction will thermal energy flow between objects C and D?

2   What does it mean to say that object X is at a higher temperature than object Y?

3   What can you say about the internal energy of a steel bar at 0 K (absolute zero)?

4   Convert the following temperatures in °C to K: 0 °C, –50 °C.

5   Convert the following temperatures from K to °C: 0 K, 100 K, 300 K, 373 K.

6   Which temperature is higher, 145 K or –130 °C?

Specific heat capacity

Key words

- specific heat capacity
- latent heat

Hint

The word specific here means per unit mass or per kilogram.

✓ *Quick check 1*

When a substance is heated, its temperature rises (unless it changes state – see pages 20–21). Taking equal masses, some substances heat up more quickly than others – they have a low **specific heat capacity (s.h.c.)**.

Defining s.h.c.

Energy must be supplied to raise the temperature of a substance. The amount of energy E that must be supplied depends on:

- the mass of the substance, m
- its specific heat capacity (s.h.c.), c
- the temperature rise, $\Delta\theta$.

The specific heat capacity of a substance is the amount of energy needed to raise the temperature of 1 kg of the substance by 1 °C, or by 1 K.

Calculations

The four quantities above are related by the equation

$$E = mc\Delta\theta$$

Rearranging this equation gives

specific heat capacity $c = \dfrac{E}{m\Delta\theta}$

s.h.c. = energy per kg per °C

Compare this with the definition of s.h.c. above.

Units Temperature rise $\Delta\theta$ is measured in K (kelvin). A rise of 1 K is the same as a rise of 1 °C. The units of specific heat capacity c are therefore $J\ kg^{-1}\ K^{-1}$.

■ **WORKED EXAMPLE**

A 5 kg mass of water is heated electrically. A total of 210 kJ of energy is supplied. By how much will the temperature of the water rise? (Specific heat capacity of water = 4200 $J\ kg^{-1}\ K^{-1}$.)

STEP 1 Write down what you know, and what you want to know:
$E = 210 \times 10^3$ J; $m = 5$ kg; $c = 4200\ J\ kg^{-1}\ K^{-1}$; $\Delta\theta = ?$

STEP 2 Rearrange the formula, substitute and solve:

$$\Delta\theta = \frac{E}{mc} = \frac{210 \times 10^3\ J}{5\ kg \times 4200\ J\ Kg^{-1}\ K^{-1}} = 10\ K$$

So the water's temperature rises by 10 K (or 10 °C).

✓ *Quick check 2 and 3*

Measuring s.h.c.

The electrical heater supplies energy at a steady rate to the insulated block of metal. The graph shows the rate of rise of the block's temperature. An ammeter and voltmeter are used to determine the heater's power (energy supplied per second).

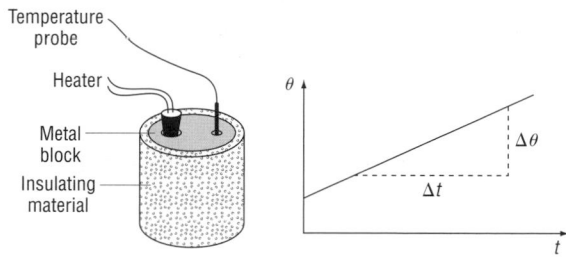

Use the straight portion of the graph to deduce the temperature rise per second, $\Delta\theta/\Delta t$. Then:

energy supplied per second = mass × s.h.c. × temperature rise per second

Practical points:

- Insulation helps to reduce the loss of energy from the block.
- Some energy is wasted in heating the thermometer and the heater itself.

Energy losses mean that the value of c deduced from this experiment is too high.

Latent heat

Energy must be supplied to melt or boil a substance. The temperature does not rise during such a *change of state*:

Latent heat of fusion is the energy which must be supplied to fuse a substance (melt it).

Latent heat of vaporisation is the energy which must be supplied to vaporise a substance (change it from liquid to gas).

QUICK CHECK QUESTIONS

1 The graph shows the results of an experiment in which samples of two different materials, each of mass 2 kg, were supplied with thermal energy at the same rate. Which material, A or B, has the greater specific heat capacity?

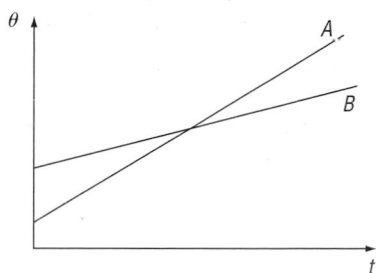

2 How much energy must be supplied to raise the temperature of a 0.5 kg block of aluminium from 20 °C to 60 °C? (s.h.c. of aluminium = 900 J kg⁻¹ K⁻¹.)

3 A 2.5 kg block of nylon at 20 °C is heated for 5 minutes using a 100 W heater. To what value will its temperature rise? (s.h.c. of nylon = 470 J kg⁻¹ K⁻¹.)

4 The graph shows the results of an experiment to measure the specific heat capacity of brass. A 1 kg block was heated with a 50 W electrical heater. Use this information to estimate the specific heat capacity of brass.

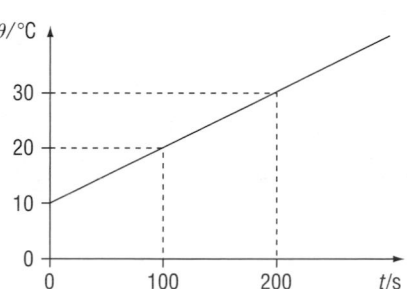

5 Describe how you would use an electrical method to determine the specific heat capacity of water. State how you would deduce the value from your measurements, and explain how any sources of error in the experiment would affect the result.

How gases behave

Key words

- Boyle's law
- kinetic theory of gases

Gases have four important, interlinked properties: mass, volume, pressure and temperature. Here we look at how these are related to each other, according to experimental evidence. On pages 28–29, we consider the idea of an *ideal gas*.

Boyle's law

Robert Boyle investigated how the volume, V, of a gas depends on its pressure, p. He had to ensure that the two other variables were fixed:

- He used a fixed mass of gas.

- He kept the gas at a fixed temperature.

Hint

The subscripts 1 and 2 refer to values of p and V before and after a change.

Increasing the pressure on a gas reduces its volume, so p and V are inversely related. Boyle was able to show that volume was inversely proportional to pressure. We can write this relationship in three ways:

$$p \propto 1/V \qquad pV = \text{constant} \qquad p_1V_1 = p_2V_2$$

These equations, and the graphs, all represent **Boyle's law**:

Hint

For a fixed mass of gas, the volume is inversely proportional to the pressure, provided the temperature remains constant.

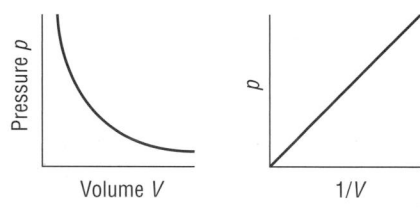

■ WORKED EXAMPLE

A cylinder contains air at a pressure of 50 kPa. Its volume is 250 cm³. Calculate the pressure required to compress the air to a volume of 100 cm³.

STEP 1 Write down what you know and what you want to know.
$p_1 = 50$ kPa; $V_1 = 250$ cm³; $V_2 = 100$ cm³; $p_2 = ?$
STEP 2 Rearrange the equation $p_1V_1 = p_2V_2$ to make p_2 the subject:
$p_2 = p_1V_1/V_2$
STEP 3 Substitute values and calculate the result:
$p_2 = 50$ kPa $\times$ 250 cm³/100 cm³ = 125 kPa.

Note that this equation works with any units of pressure (Pa, kPa, atm etc.) or volume (m³, cm³, litres etc).

✓ *Quick check 1, 2 and 3*

Three variables

Hint

Note that, in these equations, temperature T is in K.

Both pressure and volume of a fixed mass of gas increase as the temperature of the gas increases. Both are proportional to the absolute temperature T. Hence we have $P \propto T$ and $V \propto T$. These relationships can be combined with Boyle's law to give:

$$pV/T = \text{constant} \qquad p_1V_1/T_1 = p_2V_2/T_2$$

These relationships apply to a gas with low density and which is not close to its boiling point. (If a gas is cooled close to its boiling point, it will start to condense so that values of p and V no longer follow the simple relationships above.)

■ WORKED EXAMPLE

A rigid cylinder contains air at a pressure of 600 kPa and temperature of 27 °C. If the temperature of the gas is raised to 300 °C, calculate the new pressure of the air.

STEP 1 Write down what you know and what you want to know.

$p_1 = 600$ kPa; $T_1 = 27$ °C $= 300$ K, $T_2 = 300$ °C $= 573$ K, $p_2 = ?$

(Note that temperatures must be converted to K.)

STEP 2 Rearrange the equation $p_1V_1/T_1 = p_2V_2/T_2$ to make p_2 the subject: we can also cancel V_1 and V_2 because V does not change:

$p_2 = p_1T_2/T_1$

STEP 3 Substitute values and calculate the result:

$p_2 = 600$ kPa $\times 573$ K$/300$ K $= 1146$ kPa ~ 1150 kPa

(The absolute temperature of the gas has almost doubled, so its pressure has almost doubled.)

Examiner tip

Note that, because the cylinder is rigid, the volume V of the air does not change.

✓*Quick check 4 and 5*

Ideal and real gases

Any gas which obeys the relationship $pV/T =$ constant is described as an **ideal gas**. As noted above, real gases can deviate from ideal behaviour, especially when they are close to their boiling point.

Hint

More about ideal gases on pages 28–29.

Kinetic theory of gases

To explain the observed behaviour of gases, scientists developed the **kinetic theory of gases**. Its assumptions are:

• The molecules of the gas are in rapid random motion.

• Their volume is negligible compared with the volume of the gas.

• The molecules undergo perfectly elastic collisions.

• They exert no forces on other molecules or the container except during collisions.

• The time spent in collisions is small compared to the time between collisions.

From these assumptions, the relationship $pV/T =$ constant can be deduced.

✓*Quick check 6*

QUICK CHECK QUESTIONS

1 The pressure on a container of gas is doubled. What will happen to its volume? (What assumptions are made in answering this?)

2 A closed cylinder contains 400 litres of nitrogen at a pressure of 3.2 atm. A piston compresses the gas to a pressure of 8.0 atm. Calculate its new volume.

3 A container holds 450 m³ of natural gas at a pressure of 800 kPa. The gas expands so that its volume becomes 2000 m³. Calculate its new pressure.

4 If the absolute temperature of a fixed mass of an ideal gas is doubled, how will its pressure change? (Assume that its volume is fixed.)

5 A container holds 20 m³ of an ideal gas at a pressure of 100 kPa and a temperature of 20 °C. If the container is heated to 380 °C and it expands to 25 m³, calculate the new pressure of the gas.

6 The kinetic theory of gases assumes that the collisions between molecules of a gas are perfectly elastic. Explain what this means.

Examiner tip

In this example, all three variables are changing.

Ideal gases

The **equation of state for an ideal gas** (also called the **ideal gas equation**) relates the pressure, volume and temperature of a gas. We can also relate these quantities to the average kinetic energy of the molecules of the gas. In these relationships, the amount of a gas is expressed in *moles*.

The mole and the Avogadro constant

The **mole** (abbreviated to **mol**) is the unit of *amount* of a substance. One mole of any substance consists of a standard number of particles. This number is N_A, the **Avogadro constant**:

$$N_A = 6.02 \times 10^{23} \text{ mol}^{-1}$$

The mass of one mole of any substance is the relative molecular mass of the substance, expressed in grams.

For example, the relative molecular mass of water is 18, so 1 mole of water has a mass of 18 g and consists of 6.02×10^{23} molecules.

✓ *Quick check 1*

The equation of state for an ideal gas

The pressure p (in pascals, Pa), volume V (m^3) and *absolute* temperature T (K) of a gas are related by

$$pV = nRT$$

where n is the number of moles of gas, and R is the **molar gas constant**:

$$R = 8.3 \text{ J K}^{-1} \text{ mol}^{-1}$$

An **ideal gas** is one that obeys $pV = nRT$. In practice, most gases behave ideally only at low pressures and at temperatures well above their boiling points.

Examiner tip

Always express temperatures in kelvin (see page 41) when applying this equation.

Examiner tip

If you are studying chemistry, you should recognise this as the volume of 1 mole at standard temperature and pressure (s.t.p.).

✓ *Quick check 2 and 3*

■ WORKED EXAMPLE

What volume is occupied by 1 mole of a gas at a pressure of 10^5 Pa and a temperature of 273 K?

STEP 1 Write down what you know, and what you want to know:
$n = 1$ mol; $p = 10^5$ Pa; $T = 273$ K; $R = 8.3$ J K^{-1} mol^{-1}; $V = ?$

STEP 2 Rearrange the equation of state, substitute and solve:

$$V = \frac{nRT}{P} = \frac{1 \text{ mol} \times 8.3 \text{ J K}^{-1} \text{ mol}^{-1} \times 273 \text{ K}}{10^5 \text{ Pa}}$$
$$= 0.0227 \text{ m}^3$$

Note that, using SI units throughout, the volume is in m^3.

Number of molecules

The ideal gas equation can also be expressed in terms of the number of molecules, N, in the gas. In this case we have

$pV = NkT$

where k is the **Boltzmann constant**, related to R by

$R = N_A k$
$k = 1.38 \times 10^{-23}$ J K^{-1}

✔*Quick check 4*

Molecular energy

The molecules of a gas have a range of speeds – some are moving faster than others. At higher temperatures, they move faster on average. Their mean translational kinetic energy is proportional to the absolute temperature.

average translational kinetic energy of an atom ∝ **absolute temperature**

mean translational kinetic energy $E = 3/2\, kT$

For example, at 300 K, the mean kinetic energy of an atom in a gas = $3/2 \times 1.38 \times 10^{-23} \times 300 = 6.2 \times 10^{-21}$ J; some atoms have more translational kinetic energy than this, others have less.

> **Hint**
>
> When we measure the absolute temperature of a gas, we are measuring the average kinetic energy of its molecules.

Module 3

✔*Quick check 5 and 6*

QUICK CHECK QUESTIONS

1 How many particles are there in 5 moles of water? In 5 moles of uranium?

2 At what temperature will 10 moles of an ideal gas occupy 0.1 m^3 at a pressure of 2×10^5 Pa? (Molar gas constant $R = 8.3$ J K^{-1} mol^{-1}.)

3 An ideal gas initially occupies a volume of 10 litres. It is compressed at a constant temperature so that its pressure increases by a factor of 2.5. Calculate its new volume.

4 A sample of oxygen contains 2.4×10^{23} molecules at a temperature of 250 K and a pressure of 85 kPa. Calculate the volume occupied by the gas.

5 A gas is heated from 300 K to 600 K at a constant pressure. What happens to the average kinetic energy of its molecules during this process? The gas is then compressed to half its original volume, still at 600 K. What happens to the average kinetic energy of the molecules during this second process?

6 Calculate the mean translational kinetic energy of the oxygen molecules in Question 4.

End-of-unit questions

See Appendix 3 on page 78 for data and formulae provided in the examination.

Module 1 – Newton's laws and momentum

1 (a) Define (linear) momentum and state whether it is a vector or scalar quantity.
  (b) Calculate the momentum of a bus of mass 6000 kg moving at 20 m s^{-1}.
  (c) State the principle of conservation of momentum.
  (d) Explain how the principle of conservation of momentum applies in the following situations:
    (i) a child, initially stationary, jumps up in the air;
    (ii) the child lands on the ground (without bouncing).

2 (a) What is meant by an *elastic* collision?
  (b) A marble of mass 5 g moving at 1 m s^{-1} collides with an identical, stationary marble. The first marble stops dead and the second moves off at 1 m s^{-1}.
    (i) Show that momentum is conserved in this collision.
    (ii) Show that this collision is elastic.

3 A cannon of mass 500 kg fires a shell of mass 2.5 kg. The cannon recoils with a velocity of 2.4 m s^{-1}. Calculate the initial velocity of the shell.

4 A trolley of mass 2.0 kg and moving at 2.1 m s^{-1} collides with a second, stationary trolley of mass 1.5 kg. The two trolleys move off together.
  (a) Calculate their shared velocity.
  (b) Show that kinetic energy is not conserved in this collision.
  (c) Give the term which describes a collision in which kinetic energy is not conserved.

5 A force of 20 N acts on a box of mass 48 kg. The force acts for 3.0 s.
  (a) Calculate the impulse of the force.
  (b) State the change in momentum of the box.
  (c) If the box is initially stationary, what is its velocity after 3 s?

6 A 5 kg mass (A) travelling at 10 m s^{-1} collides with an identical mass (B) travelling in the same direction at 6 m s^{-1}.
  (a) If the collision is perfectly elastic, what will be the velocities of the two masses after the collision?
  (b) If the two masses stick together, what will be their shared velocity after the collision?

7 Two marbles (solid spheres) travelling with equal but opposite velocities *v* and *–v* collide head-on. Describe the possible motions of the two marbles:
  (a) if their collision is perfectly elastic;
  (b) if their collision is inelastic.

Module 2 – Circular motion and oscillations

8 (a) An electron follows a circular orbit of radius *r* around the nucleus of an atom. Draw a diagram to represent this. Include arrows to show:
  • the electron's velocity *v*;
  • the centripetal force *F* acting on the electron.

(b) Write down an expression for F in terms of v, r and the electron's mass m.

9 A toy train travels round a circular track at a steady speed. It completes three orbits in 1.0 minutes. The radius of curvature of the track is 40 cm.
   (a) Calculate the speed of the train.
   (b) Calculate the angular velocity of the train. Give your answer in rad s^{-1}.

10 Jupiter has mass M; one of its moons has mass m and orbits along a circular path of radius r.
   (a) Write down an expression for the gravitational force F that Jupiter exerts on its moon. What can you say about the gravitational force exerted by this moon on Jupiter?
   (b) The moon orbits Jupiter with speed v. Use the data below to calculate v.
   - Mass of Jupiter $M = 1.9 \times 10^{27}$ kg
   - Radius of moon's orbit $r = 7.0 \times 10^5$ km
   - Universal gravitational constant $G = 6.67 \times 10^{-11}$ N m^2 kg^{-2}
   (c) Calculate the duration of one complete orbit of Jupiter.

11 **(a)** Define *geostationary orbit* of a satellite.
   (b) Describe the orbit of a geostationary satellite around the Earth.
   (c) State two uses of geostationary satellites.

12 A small mass hangs from the end of a light spring. It is displaced slightly downwards and released. It oscillates up and down with simple harmonic motion. Its oscillations are represented by the graph.

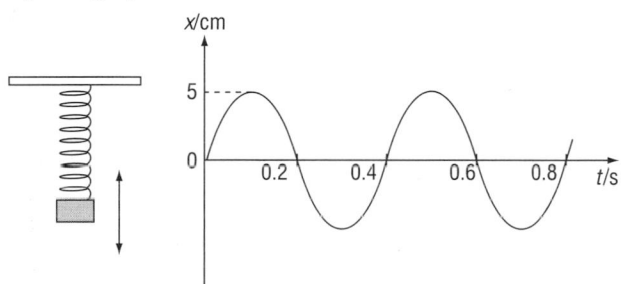

   (a) State what is meant by *simple harmonic motion*.
   (b) What are the amplitude, period and frequency of the oscillations?
   (c) Mark with an A on the graph one point at which the acceleration is a maximum.
   (d) Mark with a V on the graph one point at which the velocity is a maximum.
   (e) Write down an equation to represent the mass's displacement x as a function of time t. Use your equation to deduce the mass's displacement when $t = 20$ s.
   (f) Calculate the maximum value of the mass's acceleration.

13 A vibrating object of mass 0.10 kg oscillates with simple harmonic motion of amplitude 10.0 cm. It completes 400 oscillations in 6.0 s.
   (a) Calculate the frequency of the oscillations.
   (b) Write an equation of the form $a = kx$ relating the object's acceleration to its displacement.
   (c) At what points in the object's motion does its acceleration have its maximum value?
   (d) Calculate the maximum value of the object's acceleration.

14 A prototype washing machine was tested by placing it on a test bed and gradually increasing the frequency of rotation of the electric motor. The amplitude of vibration of the top surface of the washing machine was measured over the range of motor frequencies. Resonance occurred when the motor frequency was 65 Hz, with a corresponding amplitude of 1.2 mm.

(a) Explain what is meant by *resonance*.
(b) Sketch a graph of amplitude (*y*-axis) against frequency (*x*-axis) for the test results.
(c) Explain what is meant by a *damped* vibration.
(d) On the same set of axes you used in (b), sketch the effect of applying more damping to the vibrations.

15 A satellite is required to orbit the Earth once every 12 hours. Calculate the necessary radius of its orbit and its orbital speed.
[mass of Earth = 6.0×10^{24} kg]

16 A cylindrical wooden rod is weighted at its lower end so that it floats vertically in water. The rod is pushed gently downwards and released. Show that its subsequent motion will be simple harmonic.

Module 3 – Thermal physics

17 A sample of lead is heated from 10 °C below its melting point to 10 °C above its melting point. The graph shows how its temperature changes with time.

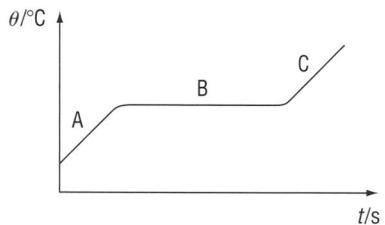

(a) For each of sections A–C of the graph, state how the lead's internal energy is changing.
(b) The lead is made up of atoms. For each of sections A–C, state how the atoms' kinetic and potential energies are changing.
(c) 60 J of energy must be supplied to raise the temperature of a 50 g sample of solid lead by 10 °C. Calculate the specific heat capacity of tin.
(d) What is meant by the term *latent heat of fusion*?

18 Describe an experiment to determine the specific heat capacity of aluminium, using an electrical method to heat the aluminium. Your description should briefly outline:
• the equipment used;
• the measurements to be made;
• an explanation of how the value of the specific heat capacity can be determined from the results;
• any likely sources of error and their effect on the final answer.

19 (a) Define *internal energy* of a body.
(b) At what temperature does a body have minimum internal energy? Give your answer:
(i) on the thermodynamic scale;
(ii) on the Celsius scale.

20 (a) State Boyle's law.
(b) A mass of gas has a volume of 24 litres at a pressure of 150 kPa. Calculate the pressure required to reduce the volume of the gas to 16 litres at constant temperature.

21 (a) One mole of oxygen consists of 6.02×10^{23} molecules. Of what quantity is the mole the unit?

(b) Write down an equation linking the pressure p and volume V of 1 mole of an ideal gas to its absolute temperature T.

(c) Use your equation to calculate the pressure of 1 mole of oxygen at 100 °C if it occupies a volume of 0.025 m³.

22 (a) The equation $pV = NkT$ relates the pressure p and volume V of a gas to its absolute temperature T. Explain the meaning of the symbol N in this equation.

(b) A sample of 1 mole of a gas occupies a volume of 0.05 m³ when its pressure is 5×10^4 Pa. Calculate the mean translational kinetic energy of its particles.

23 The thermodynamic temperature of a gas is increased from 30 °C to 140 °C. By what factor does the mean translational kinetic energy of its molecules increase?

24 The air around you contains molecules of oxygen (O_2) and carbon dioxide (CO_2). Explain why the average speed of a molecule of carbon dioxide is lower than that of a molecule of oxygen.

UNIT 2

Fields, particles and frontiers of physics

There are five modules in this unit.

Module 1: Electric and magnetic fields looks at how we can represent the force fields around electrical charges (stationary and moving) and around magnets and electromagnets. It considers the forces which arise in these fields and how they can be used.

Module 2: Capacitors and exponential decay will introduce you to some uses of capacitors in electric circuits. It will show you how we can analyse the discharge of a capacitor mathematically.

Module 3: Nuclear physics looks at atomic and sub-atomic particles. In dealing with radioactive decay, it uses a similar approach to that introduced for capacitor discharge in Module 2.

Module 4: Medical imaging deals with techniques from physics which are used in medical diagnosis and treatment.

Module 5: Modelling the universe considers what we know about the matter and energy which make up the universe as a whole, its history and possible future.

This unit counts for 50% of your A2 examination (25% of the total Advanced GCE qualification).

There is one experiment that you must be able to describe as part of unit 2 (G485) for the examination. This is the alpha-particle scattering experiment used to show the existence and nature of the atomic nucleus (page 48).

For this experiment, you should be able to:

- sketch the appropriate apparatus and label it
- describe the measurements made
- give a qualitative description of the results
- explain how these are accounted for by the nuclear model of the atom.

Module 1 – Electric and magnetic fields, pages 36–43

Topic (in this book)	Reference to specification	Ideas from GCSE and AS
Electric fields	5.1.1 a–c, f–g	Representing fields with lines of force
Coulomb's law	5.1.1 d–e, h	Forces between static charges
Magnetic fields and forces	5.1.2 a–h	Electric motors and motor effect
Electromagnetic induction	5.1.3 a–k	Electrical generators

Module 2 – Capacitors and exponential decay, pages 44–47

Topic (in this book)	Reference to specification	Ideas from GCSE and AS
Capacitors	5.2.1 a–g, m	Current and charge, voltage, electrical energy
Discharging a capacitor	5.2.1 h–l	Radioactive decay graphs

Module 3 – Nuclear physics, pages 48–57

Topic (in this book)	Reference to specification	Ideas from GCSE and AS
Atomic structure	5.3.1 a–h	Protons, neutrons, electrons
Nuclear processes and forces	5.3.1 i–j, 5.3.2 a–j	α, β, γ radiation
Mass – energy conservation	5.3.4 a–m	Conservation laws
Radioactive decay	5.3.3 a–d	Nature of α, β, γ
Radioactive decay equations	5.3.3 e–j	Half-life and background radiation

Module 4 – Medical physics, pages 58–63

Topic (in this book)	Reference to specification	Ideas from GCSE and AS
X-rays	5.4.1 a–i	Electromagnetic spectrum, intensity
Diagnostic methods in medicine	5.4.2 a–h	Ionising radiation, magnetic fields
Ultrasound in medicine	5.4.2 i–j, 5.4.3 a–i	Refraction of light

Module 5 – Modelling the Universe, pages 64–69

Topic (in this book)	Reference to specification	Ideas from GCSE and AS
The structure of the universe	5.5.1 a–i, n	The solar system
The expanding universe	5.5.1 j–m, 5.5.2 b	Light as a wave
The evolution of the universe	5.5.1 o, 5.5.2 a, c–h	Gravitational fields, density

End-of-unit questions, pages 70–73

UNIT 2

Electric fields

Key words
- electric field
- field lines
- electric field strength

In Unit 1, you studied gravitational fields. These are created by objects with mass. **Electric fields** are created by objects with electric charge. One important difference is that there is only one type of mass, but there are two types of charge, *positive* and *negative*. Therefore electrostatic forces can be *attractive* or *repulsive*, whereas gravitational forces are always attractive.

Field lines

An electric field can be represented by **field lines**, rather like a gravitational field.

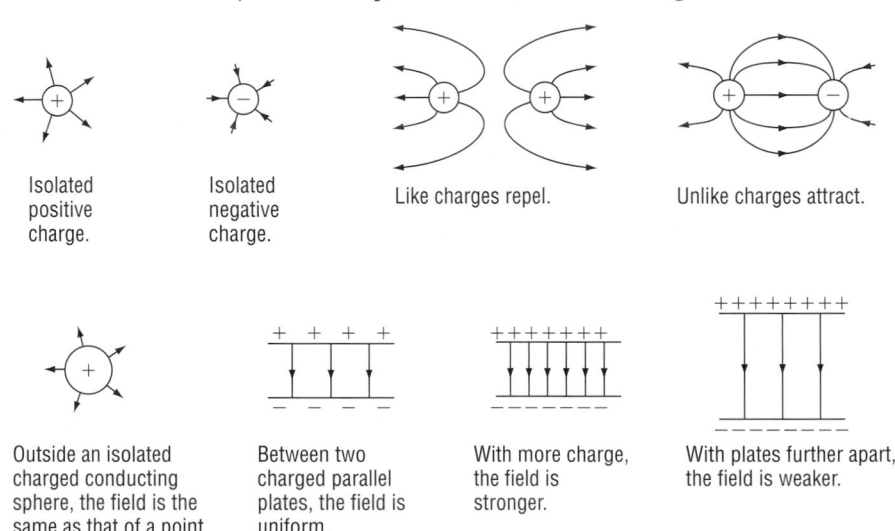

Isolated positive charge.

Isolated negative charge.

Like charges repel.

Unlike charges attract.

Outside an isolated charged conducting sphere, the field is the same as that of a point charge at its centre.

Between two charged parallel plates, the field is uniform.

With more charge, the field is stronger.

With plates further apart, the field is weaker.

- The arrows show the direction of the force on a *positive* charge placed in the field.
- Arrows come out of positive charges, and go into negative charges.
- Lines closer together represent a stronger field.

✔*Quick check 1*

Electric field strength

An electric field is a field of force. Any charged object placed in the field will feel a force. To define the **electric field strength** at a point in the field, we picture placing a unit positive charge at the point. The force acting on the unit positive charge is the electric field strenght E. For a charge Q placed at that point the force F acting on it is

$$F = EQ$$

The unit of electric charge is the *coulomb* (C). The unit of E is therefore *newtons per coulomb* (N C^{-1}).

Hint

For electric charge and the coulomb, see AS Unit 2 Module 1, page 34 of the Revision Guide.

Recall from AS Unit 2 (page 37) that one volt is the work done (in joules) in pushing one coulomb of charge round a complete circuit: $1V = 1 \text{ J C}^{-1}$. Also, from Module A, page 16, $1 \text{ J} = 1 \text{ N} \times 1 \text{ m}$. Therefore:

$$1 \text{ N C}^{-1} = 1 \text{ J m}^{-1} \text{ C}^{-1} = 1 \text{ V m}^{-1}$$

✔*Quick check 2*

So electric field strength can also be expressed in *volts per metre*.

Charged parallel plates

There is a uniform electric field between a pair of parallel plates. The plates can be charged by applying a voltage across them. The greater the voltage, the stronger the field.

strength of field $E = \dfrac{V}{d}$

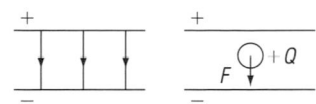

This is easily recalled if you remember that electric field strength can be measured in volts per metre (see above).

Now we have two equations for E:

$$E = \frac{F}{Q} \text{ and } E = \frac{V}{d}$$

Putting these equal gives $F/Q = V/d$, and hence

$Fd = QV$

Thus the work done (Fd) in moving a charge Q through p.d. V is equal to QV.

This is the equation that defines the volt: $W = QV$ (see AS Unit 2, page 37).

✔ *Quick check 3, 4 and 5*

Motion in a uniform field

A charged particle moves in a uniform electric field in the same way that a mass moves in a uniform gravitational field:

A charge which is initially stationary will accelerate in a straight line.

A charge which is moving across the field will follow a curved (parabolic) path.

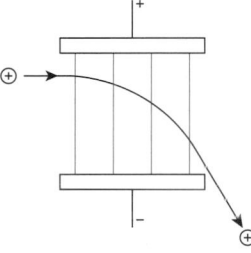

✔ *Quick check 6*

QUICK CHECK QUESTIONS

1 Copy the diagram, which shows two charged parallel metal plates. Add field lines to show the electric field between the plates. Explain how your diagram shows that this field is uniform.

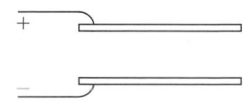

2 An electron is moving through an electric field of strength 10 kN C⁻¹. What is the electric force on it? (Charge on an electron $e = 1.6 \times 10^{-19}$ C.)

3 Two parallel plates separated by 20 cm are connected to the terminals of a 60 V power supply. Calculate the electric field strength in the space between them.

4 Use the equation $E = V/d$ to explain the following:
   - increasing the p.d. between a pair of parallel plates increases the field strength between them;
   - increasing the separation of the plates decreases the field strength between them.

5 A dust particle carrying a charge of 4 mC is in the space between two parallel plates separated by 5 cm. If the plates are charged to 24 V, calculate the electric force on the dust particle.

6 A positively charged particle is placed between two horizontal, parallel plates. The lower plate has a positive charge while the upper plate has a negative charge. Describe and explain how the particle will move when it is released.

UNIT 2 Coulomb's law

Key words

- Coulomb's law
- permittivity of free space

The electric field around a charged sphere or point charge is *radial*, like the gravitational field around a spherical mass. **Coulomb's law** tells us how to calculate the force between two spherical charges.

Force between two spherical charges

The electrostatic force F between two charges Q and q separated by a distance r is given by Coulomb's law:

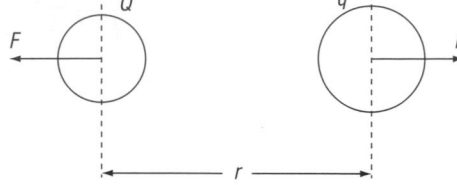

$$F = \frac{kQq}{r^2}$$

Hint

Like Newton's law of gravitation (page 16), this is an example of an *inverse square law*: F is proportional to $1/r^2$.

The value of the constant k is approximately 9×10^9 N m² C⁻². It is usually written as $k = 1/(4\pi\varepsilon_0)$, where ε_0 is called the **permittivity of free space**.

$$F = \frac{Qq}{4\pi\varepsilon_0 r^2}$$

✓*Quick check 1*

The charges are *point charges*, as if all of an object's charge is concentrated at a point. Each of the two charges feels the same force (even if their charges are different), but in opposite directions. They are an equal and opposite pair of forces, as described by Newton's third law of motion (page 6).

■ WORKED EXAMPLE

In an oxygen atom, the outermost electron orbits the nucleus at a distance of approximately 0.09 nm. The electron charge is $-e$ and the nuclear charge is $+8e$, where $e = 1.6 \times 10^{-19}$ C. Calculate the electrostatic force exerted by the nucleus on the electron.

Examiner tip

There is no need to move the decimal point for r; your calculator will cope.

STEP 1 Write down the known values of quantities:
$k = 9 \times 10^9$ N m² C⁻²
$Q = e = 1.6 \times 10^{-19}$ C
$q = 8e = 8 \times 1.6 \times 10^{-19}$ C $= 1.28 \times 10^{-18}$ C
$r = 0.09$ nm $= 0.09 \times 10^{-9}$ m

STEP 2 Write down the equation for Coulomb's law. Substitute values and calculate F:

Examiner tip

Note how the units cancel correctly to leave N.

$$F = \frac{kQq}{r^2}$$

$$= \frac{9 \times 10^9 \text{ N m}^2 \times 1.6 \times 10^{-19} \text{ C} \times 1.28 \times 10^{-18} \text{ C}}{(0.09 \times 10^{-9} \text{ m})^2}$$

$$= 2.3 \times 10^{-7} \text{ N}$$

✓*Quick check 2*

E for a point charge

For a point charge Q, the electric field strength E at a distance r is

$$E = \frac{kQ}{r^2}$$

This comes from dividing the Coulomb's law equation by q.

Comparing gravitational and electric fields

	Gravitational field	Electric field
Origin	any object with mass	any object with charge
Field strength equation	$g = F/m$	$E = F/Q$
Radial field	point mass or spherical mass	point charge or charged sphere
Inverse square law	Newton's law: $F = \dfrac{GMm}{r^2}$	Coulomb's law: $F = \dfrac{kQq}{r^2}$
Constant	$G = 6.67 \times 10^{-11}$ N m² kg⁻²	$k = 9 \times 10^{9}$ N m² C⁻²
Uniform field	near surface of Earth $g \sim 9.8$ N kg⁻¹	between charged parallel plates $E = V/d$

The equation $g = F/m$ can be applied in *any* gravitational field, and $E = F/Q$ in *any* electric field. The other equations can be applied only in radial or uniform fields, as appropriate.

QUICK CHECK QUESTIONS

1 Draw a diagram to show two negative point charges. Add arrows to represent the force each charge exerts on the other. What can you say about the magnitudes and directions of these forces?

2 Calculate the electric force between two protons in the nucleus of an atom, separated by 10^{-15} m. (Proton charge = $+e = +1.6 \times 10^{-19}$ C.)

3 A metal sphere of radius 5 cm carries a charge of 40 mC. Calculate the electric field strength at a distance of 1 cm from the surface of the sphere. ($k = 1/4\pi\varepsilon_0 = 9 \times 10^{9}$ N m² C⁻².)

Magnetic fields and forces

An electric current has a *magnetic field* around it. The diagrams show the field lines for:

- a long straight wire – the field lines are circles around the wire;
- a long solenoid – there is a magnetic pole at each end.

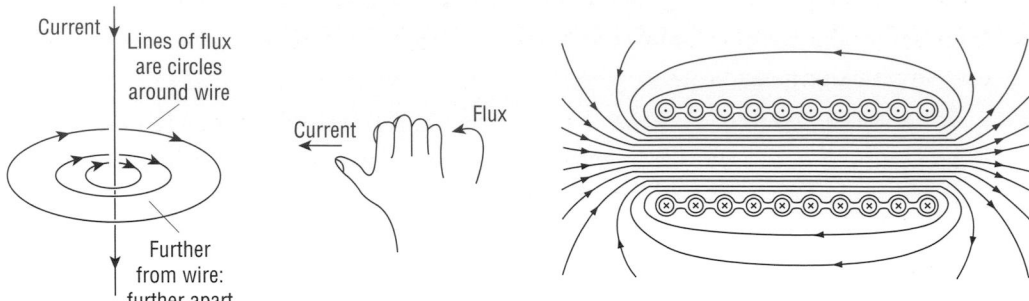

The strength of a field is described by its **flux density**, *B*, and the unit of measurement is the **tesla** (T). A field with a high flux density is represented by field lines which are close together.

✔ *Quick check 1*

Force on a current-carrying conductor

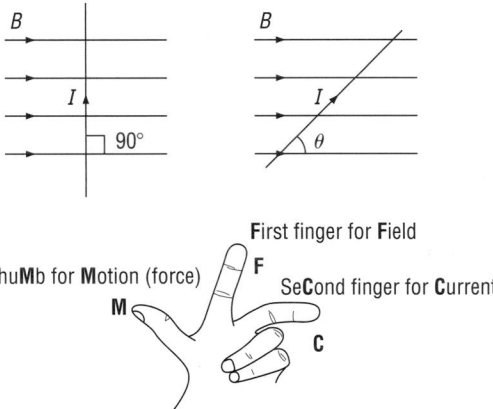

First finger for **Field**

ThuMb for Motion (force)

SeCond finger for Current

If a current flows *across* another magnetic field, the two fields interact to produce a force. When a current *I* flows at 90° to the magnetic flux (flux density *B*), the force *F* that acts on it is:

$$F = BIl$$

In this equation, *l* is the length of the conductor. When the conductor is at angle θ to the flux, *l* must be replaced by its component at 90° to *B*. This component is $l \sin \theta$:

$$F = BIl \sin \theta$$

- Current flowing at 90° to flux: $\theta = 90°$, $\sin \theta = 1$, $F = BIl$.
- Current flowing parallel to flux: $\theta = 0°$, $\sin \theta = 0$, $F = 0$.

The force arises only when the current flows *across* the flux. Its direction is given by *Fleming's left-hand rule* (see diagram above).

✔ *Quick check 2*

The equation $F = BIl$ defines the tesla. Rearranging gives $B = F/Il$, so $1\,T = 1\,N\,A^{-1}\,m^{-1}$.

Force on a moving charge

When a positive charge Q moves with velocity v across a field of flux density B, the force F on the charge is

$$F = BQv$$

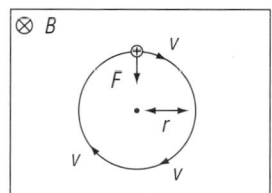

A stronger field, a greater charge and a faster charge all give a bigger force.

- Direction of the force on a *positive* charge: a current is a flow of positive charge, so use Fleming's left-hand rule.
- Direction of the force on a *negative* charge: the current is in the opposite direction to the movement of the charge, so point your second finger in the opposite direction to v when using Fleming's left-hand rule.

✔*Quick check 3*

Circular motion

When a particle with charge Q moves at 90° to a magnetic field, the force on it is always at 90° to its velocity. (This is shown by Fleming's left-hand rule.) This is the condition needed for circular motion, so the charged particle will follow a circular path and we can describe the force as a *centripetal* force (see page 10).

Magnetic force = mass × centripetal acceleration:

$$BQv = \frac{mv^2}{r}$$

Cancelling v from both sides and rearranging to find r gives

$$BQ = \frac{mv}{r} \text{ and } r = \frac{mv}{B}Q$$

Looking at this equation shows that increasing the flux density will decrease the radius of the particle's orbit, i.e. the particle will go round in tighter circles. This fact is used in a **mass spectrometer**, where charged particles (ions) of different charges and masses are separated by passing them through a magnetic field.

✔*Quick check 4, 5 and 6*

QUICK CHECK QUESTIONS

1 A long solenoid has a current flowing through it. Draw two diagrams of the solenoid, showing how the field lines differ when a small current flows and when a greater current flows.

2 A current of 5 A flows through a 2 m length of wire. The wire lies across a magnetic field of flux density 80 mT, as shown. What is the force on the wire? In which direction does the force act?

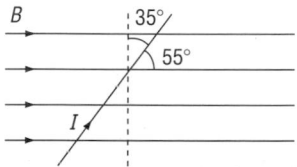

Examiner tip

In question 2, take care to use the correct angle θ in your calculation.

3 What force acts on an electron moving at 10^7 m s^{-1} at 90° to a magnetic field of flux density 0.1 T? (Electron charge $e = -1.6 \times 10^{-19}$ C.)

4 An electron enters a magnetic field as shown in the lower diagram. In which direction will the magnetic force on the electron act?

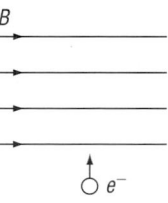

5 Calculate the radius of the orbit of the electron in Question 2. (Electron mass = 9.1×10^{-31} kg.)

6 Two electrons, moving at different speeds but in the same direction, enter a magnetic field. Which will experience the greater force? Which will move around a bigger orbit?

Electromagnetic induction

Key words

- electromagnetic induction
- weber
- flux linkage
- Faraday's law
- Lenz's law

When a conductor is moved through a magnetic field, an e.m.f. may be generated across its ends. If it is part of a complete circuit, an induced current may flow. This is **electromagnetic induction**.

Flux and flux linkage

Units Flux and flux linkage are measured in **webers** (Wb). These are related to teslas (T) by

1 tesla = 1 weber per square metre; 1 T = 1 Wb m^{-2}

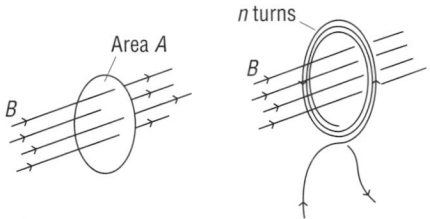

With flux density B, the flux ϕ passing through area A is given by **flux $\phi = BA$**

If the flux is at an angle θ to the area, flux $\phi = BA \cos \theta$

For a coil of n turns, the *flux linkage* is n times the flux passing through it:
flux linkage = $n\phi = nBA$

✔ *Quick check 1 and 2*

Faraday's law

To generate an *induced e.m.f.,* a conductor must be made to cut across magnetic flux. The faster it cuts flux, the greater the induced e.m.f. For a rotating coil, the faster the flux linkage through it changes, the greater the induced e.m.f. This is **Faraday's law** of electromagnetic induction, and is the basis of the electric generator.

Hint

For the difference between p.d. and e.m.f., refer back to AS Unit 2 Module 2, page 36 of the Revision Guide.

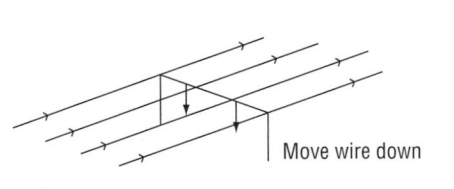
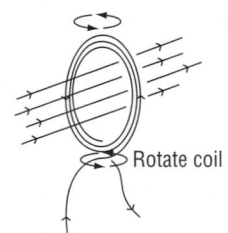

Move wire down

Rotate coil

In SI units,

induced e.m.f. = −rate of change of flux linkage

✔ *Quick check 3*

Lenz's law

This law determines the direction in which an induced current flows, or the polarity of an induced e.m.f. An induced current flows in a direction to oppose the change producing it. This is **Lenz's law.**

For example, if a straight conductor is moved across a magnetic field, an induced current flows in it. There is a force on this current, and this force opposes the force pushing the conductor across the field.

You can use *Fleming's right-hand rule* to determine the direction of an induced current. Thumb and fingers represent the same quantities as in the left-hand rule (page 40), but in this case using the right hand.

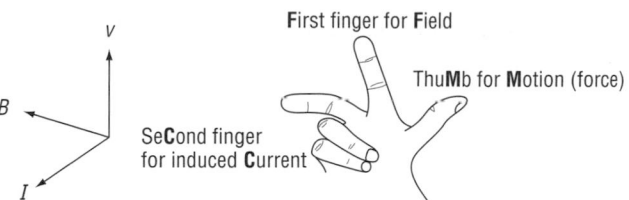

First finger for **F**ield

Thu**M**b for **M**otion (force)

Se**C**ond finger for induced **C**urrent

✓ *Quick check 4*

Transformers

A transformer has two coils, the primary with n_p turns and the secondary with n_s turns. These are linked by a core.

When an alternating current flows in the primary coil, it acts as a solenoid and produces an alternating magnetic field in the core. This field induces an e.m.f. in the secondary coil.

A *step-up* transformer has more secondary turns than primary and increases the voltage.

A *step-down* transformer has fewer secondary turns than primary and decreases the voltage.

The ratio of the primary and secondary voltages is equal to the turns ratio of the transformer:

$$\frac{V_s}{V_p} = \frac{n_s}{n_p}$$

✓ *Quick check 5*

Iron core   Iron core

Other applications of electromagnetic induction

* A coil rotating in a magnetic field (a generator).
* A magnet rotating in a coil (a bicycle dynamo).

In each case, an alternating e.m.f. is induced across the ends of the coil.

QUICK CHECK QUESTIONS

1 2×10^{-3} Wb of magnetic flux pass through a square area 10 cm × 10 cm. What is the flux density of this field?

2 What is the flux linkage of a circular coil of radius 5 cm, consisting of 50 turns of wire, placed perpendicular to a magnetic field of flux density 200 mT?

3 A coil of wire is being rotated in a magnetic field. Which of the following will increase the e.m.f. induced across the coil: increasing the flux density of the field; increasing the rate of rotation; reversing the direction of rotation; reducing the resistance of the coil by using thicker wire?

4 The straight conductor shown is being pushed across a uniform magnetic field. Will the induced current flow towards or away from point A? Will point A acquire a positive or a negative charge?

Flux downwards into page

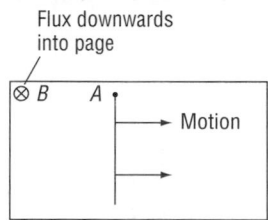

⊗ B   A

Motion

5 A transformer has 20 turns on its primary coil and 400 on its secondary. What is its turns ratio? If a 12 V a.c. supply is connected to the primary, what will its output e.m.f. be?

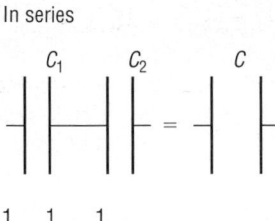

Capacitors

Key words

- capacitance
- charge
- voltage

Capacitors are components used in circuits to store electric **charge**. They usually consist of two parallel metal plates, separated by a narrow gap.

Stored charge

When a capacitor is connected to a source of **voltage** (p.d.), one plate gains positive charge $+Q$, while the other gains negative charge $-Q$. The capacitor is said to be storing Q coulombs of charge.

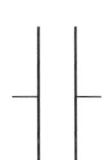 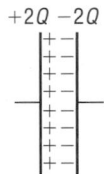 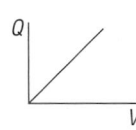

Increasing the voltage pushes more charge onto the capacitor. The greater the voltage V and the greater the **capacitance** C of the capacitor, the more charge Q it stores. This is represented by the equation

charge stored = p.d. × capacitance $Q = VC$

Definitions

The equation $Q = VC$ can be rearranged to define capacitance:

$$C = \frac{Q}{V}$$

The capacitance of a capacitor is the charge stored for each volt of p.d. across it.

Units Capacitance is measured in **farads** (F). One farad is one coulomb per volt. Most practical capacitors have values measured in smaller units (see Appendix 2):

- 1 μF = 1 microfarad = 10^{-6} F

- 1 pF = 1 picofarad = 10^{-12} F

✓ *Quick check 1*

Capacitors in series and in parallel

Note that these are similar to the formulae for combining resistances (AS Unit 2, Module 3, pages 46–47), but the other way round, with the reciprocal formula (1/C) for capacitances in series but for resistors in parallel.

In series

$$\frac{1}{C} = \frac{1}{C_1} + \frac{1}{C_2} + \cdots$$

In series: combined capacitance is less than each individual capacitance.

In parallel

$$C = C_1 + C_2 + \cdots$$

In parallel: combined capacitance is the sum of the individual capacitances.

✓ *Quick check 2 and 3*

Examiner tip

Note that we can work in μF, without writing the powers of 10.

WORKED EXAMPLE

What is the capacitance of a 20 μF and a 30 μF capacitor connected in series?

STEP 1 Write down the appropriate formula, substitute values and add the fractions:

$$\frac{1}{C} = \frac{1}{C_1} + \frac{1}{C_2} = \frac{1}{20 \mu F} + \frac{1}{30 \mu F} = \frac{5}{60 \mu F} = \frac{1}{12 \mu F}$$

STEP 2 Take the reciprocal to find C:

$$C = 12 \mu F$$

Examiner tip

If you prefer not to add fractions, use your calculator. This will give $1/C = 0.0833 \mu F^{-1}$ and $C = (1/0.0833) \mu F = 12 \mu F$.

Storing energy

When a capacitor is charged up, work is done by the p.d. that pushes the charge onto the plates. This means that a charged capacitor is a *store of energy*. The energy is stored in the electric field between the plates. The energy is released when the capacitor is discharged.

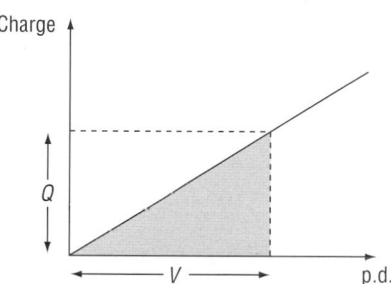

Hint

Discharging capacitors – see pages 46–47.

Since work done = energy transferred = charge × voltage, it follows that the energy W stored by a charged capacitor is the triangular area under the Q–V graph. Using the formula for the area of a triangle $\left(\frac{1}{2} \times \text{base} \times \text{height}\right)$:

energy stored $= \dfrac{1}{2} \times$ **charge** $\times$ **p.d. or** $W = \dfrac{1}{2}QV$

Substituting $Q = CV$ gives $W = \frac{1}{2}CV^2$, and substituting $V = Q/C$ gives

$W = \frac{1}{2}Q^2/C = Q^2/2C$. Hence there are three forms of the equation, the first being the fundamental one:

$$W = \frac{1}{2}QV = \frac{1}{2}CV^2 = \frac{Q^2}{2C}$$

✓ *Quick check 4*

Because capacitors can store energy and can release it quickly, they have some important applications. They are used as back-up power supplies for computers, and to power photographic flash guns. Large supercapacitors have been developed to provide the electricity needed for the lasers used in nuclear fusion research.

QUICK CHECK QUESTIONS

1   A capacitor stores 40 μC of charge when connected to a 5 V supply. What is its capacitance? How much charge will it store when connected to a 20 V supply?

2   How many 20 pF capacitors must be connected in parallel to make 100 pF?

3   What is the capacitance of three 120 μF capacitors connected in series?

4   A capacitor stores 10 mJ of energy when connected to a 100 V supply. What is its capacitance? How much energy will it store when connected to a 200 V supply?

Examiner tip

You may be able to do this a quick way, but check also that you can use the formula.

Module 2

Discharging a capacitor

When a charged capacitor is disconnected from the supply used to charge it up, it can be discharged by connecting it across a resistor. The greater the resistance, the more slowly the capacitor will discharge.

Flow of charge

Current flows round from the positively charged plate through the resistor to the negatively charged plate. As the charge decreases, so does the current.

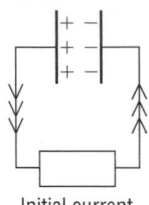
Initial current

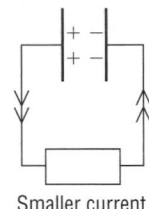
Smaller current

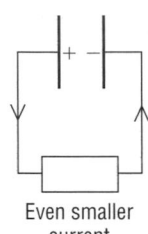
Even smaller current

Graphs

During discharge, charge Q, p.d. V and current I all follow the same pattern, an **exponential decay curve**. This curve gets closer and closer to zero, without ever reaching it.

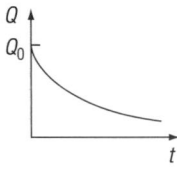

The charge stored decreases rapidly at first, then more and more slowly.

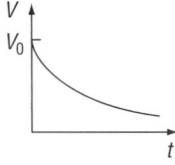

Less charge stored means less p.d. across the capacitor, so the p.d. follows the same pattern.

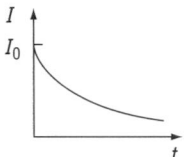

As the p.d. decreases, the current through the resistor must also decrease.

✓ *Quick check 1*

Discharge equations

$Q = Q_0 e^{-t/CR}$

Q_0 = initial charge (i.e. when $t = 0$)

$Q_0 = CV_0$

$V = V_0 e^{-t/CR}$

V_0 = initial p.d.

$V_0 = I_0 R$

$I = I_0 e^{-t/CR}$

I_0 = initial current

$I_0 = \dfrac{V_0}{R}$

These equations can be used to find values of Q, V and I at any time during the discharge. Make sure you know how to use the e^x function on your calculator – see the worked example on the next page.

We can write a more general equation – you may find it more useful to remember this single equation:

$x = x_0 e^{-t/CR}$

Replace x by Q, V or I as appropriate.

WORKED EXAMPLE

A 10 µF capacitor is charged up to 20 V, and then discharged through a 50 kΩ resistor. Calculate the initial current through the resistor, and the current after 2 s.

STEP 1 Calculate the initial current, I_0:

$$I_0 = \frac{V_0}{R} = \frac{20 \text{ V}}{50 \times 10^3 \text{ }\Omega} = 400 \text{ µA}$$

STEP 2 Using your calculator, calculate the quantity $-t/CR$, which appears in the exponential function:

$$\frac{-t}{CR} = \frac{-2}{(10 \times 10^{-6}) \times (50 \times 10^3)} = -4$$

STEP 3 Use your calculator's e^x key, then multiply by I_0:

$$I = I_0 e^{-t/CR} = 400 \text{ µA} \times e^{-4} = 7.3 \text{ µA}$$

With practice, you can merge steps 2 and 3. Always start by calculating $-t/CR$, then press e^x, then multiply by the initial value of I.

Examiner tip

The quantity $-t/CR$ has no units, so there is no need to include them.

✔ *Quick check 2 and 3*

Module 2

Time constant *CR*

The greater the value of C and the greater the value of R, the slower the discharge of a capacitor. This is because a bigger capacitor stores more charge, so it takes longer to flow away, and a bigger resistor resists the flow of charge more.

The quantity CR thus governs how quickly the capacitor discharges, and is known as the **time constant** of the circuit: symbol τ (Greek tau); units seconds (s).

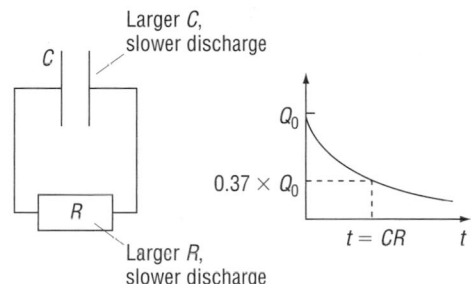

> **time constant τ = CR**

The time constant is the time for the p.d. (or charge or current) to fall to 1/e of its initial value – that is, to about 37% of the initial value. It doesn't matter which point on the graph you consider to be the starting point; it always takes the same time to decrease by a factor of 1/e.

Hint

The time constant is analogous to the half-life in radioactive decay – see page 57.

✔ *Quick check 4*

QUICK CHECK QUESTIONS

1   A capacitor is charged and discharged through a resistor. It is then charged again to the same p.d., and discharged through a resistor of twice the resistance. Which of the two graphs shown represents the second discharge? Give a reason to support your answer.

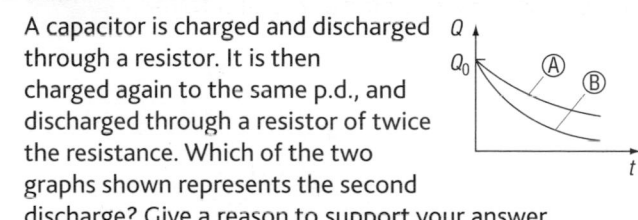

2   A 20 pF capacitor is charged up to 100 V, and then discharged through a 500 MΩ resistor. What will be the p.d. across it after 0.015 s?

3   A 12 V battery is used to charge a 1000 µF capacitor, which is then discharged through a 50 kΩ resistor. Calculate the initial current that flows, and the current after 100 s.

4   Which has the greater time constant, a circuit with a 20 µF capacitor and a 5 MΩ resistor, or a circuit with a 1000 µF capacitor and a 100 kΩ resistor?

Atomic structure

Key words

- nucleon
- proton number
- nucleon number
- isotope
- alpha particle

An atom is neutral – it contains equal amounts of positive and negative charge. The positive charge is concentrated in the tiny *nucleus* at the centre. The negative charge (of the electrons) is spread out around the nucleus.

Alpha-particle scattering

Evidence for the nuclear model of the atom comes from Rutherford's **alpha-particle scattering experiment**. (Alpha particles are positively charged helium nuclei, consisting of two protons and two neutrons.)

Evidence	Deduction
Most alpha particles pass straight through gold foil.	The atoms of the gold foil are mostly 'empty space'.
A few (about 1 in 10^4) are deflected back towards the observer.	Positive charge is concentrated in a tiny volume – the nucleus.

✔ *Quick check 1*

Relative sizes

- Diameter of nucleus ~10^{-15} m (1 fm)
- Diameter of atom ~10^{-10} m (0.1 nm)

✔ *Quick check 2 and 3*

A **molecule** may be similar in size to a single atom, or it may be much larger, depending on how many atoms it is made of. A protein molecule may have a diameter of 10^{-7} m.

Particles in an atom

Atoms are made of **protons, neutrons** and **electrons**. Protons and neutrons make up the **nucleus**, with the electrons orbiting around it.

Particle	Mass	Charge
proton	1	+1
neutron	1	0
electron	1/1840	−1

Protons and neutrons are **nucleons** (particles found in the nucleus).

Masses are given relative to the proton. The mass of a neutron is very slightly more than that of a proton.

Charges are in units of $e = 1.6 \times 10^{-19}$ C.

Representing a nucleus

- Z = **proton number** (or **atomic number**) = number of protons in nucleus
- A = **nucleon number** (or **mass number**) = number of nucleons in nucleus

In a neutral atom, number of electrons = number of protons = Z.

An individual nucleus can be represented by $^A_Z X$, e.g. $^{16}_8 O$ and $^{238}_{92} U$.

- Upper number A = nucleon number
- Lower number Z = proton number

Each combination of A and Z represents a different nuclear species or **nuclide**.

Alpha and beta particles can also be represented in this way:

- **alpha particle** (a helium nucleus – 2 protons and 2 neutrons): $^4_2 He$
- **beta particle** (an electron – zero mass, negative charge): $^0_{-1} e$

✔ *Quick check 4 and 5*

Module 3

Isotopes

Most elements come in a variety of forms or **isotopes**. Each isotope has the same number of protons in the nucleus, but different numbers of neutrons, so their masses are different.

$^1_1 H \quad ^2_1 H$
two isotopes of hydrogen

$^{54}_{26} Fe \quad ^{56}_{26} Fe$
two isotopes of iron

✔ *Quick check 6*

QUICK CHECK QUESTIONS

1   In the alpha-particle scattering experiment, Rutherford used gold foils of different thicknesses. Explain how changing the thickness of the foil would change the number of alpha particles back-scattered.

2   By how many orders of magnitude (factors of 10) does the diameter of an atom exceed that of its nucleus?

3   The smallest object resolvable using an optical microscope has a diameter of the order of 1 μm. Roughly how many atomic diameters is this?

4   Represent in symbolic form a nucleus of a silicon (Si) atom that consists of 14 protons and 14 neutrons.

5   How many protons, neutrons and electrons are there in a neutral oxygen atom whose nucleus is represented by $^{16}_8 O$?

6   The table shows the composition of four nuclei. Which nuclei are isotopes of the same element? How can you tell?

Nucleus	Number of protons	Number of neutrons
A	24	26
B	23	26
C	23	27
D	24	27

Nuclear processes and forces

Key words

- strong nuclear force
- quark
- lepton
- hadron
- antineutrino

Chemical reactions involve changes to the electrons of an atom. Nuclear reactions involve changes to the particles in the nucleus.

Representing nuclear processes

Alpha decay A nucleus emits an alpha particle, i.e. a helium nucleus (two protons and two neutrons). For example:

$$^{226}_{88}\text{Ra} \rightarrow {}^{222}_{86}\text{Rn} + {}^{4}_{2}\text{He}$$

Beta-minus decay A nucleus emits a beta particle (β^-), i.e. an electron (zero mass, negative charge). An **antineutrino** is also released. For example:

$$^{14}_{6}\text{C} \rightarrow {}^{14}_{7}\text{N} + {}^{0}_{-1}\text{e} + \bar{\nu} + \gamma$$

Beta-plus decay A nucleus emits a beta$^+$ particle (β^+), i.e. a positron (zero mass, positive charge), together with a neutrino. For example:

$$^{11}_{6}\text{C} \rightarrow {}^{11}_{5}\text{B} + {}^{0}_{+1}\text{e} + \nu + \gamma$$

Gamma decay A gamma photon (electromagnetic radiation, represented by γ) may also be emitted during alpha or beta decay (as shown in the beta-decay equations above). For example:

$$^{241}_{95}\text{Am} \rightarrow {}^{237}_{93}\text{Np} + {}^{4}_{2}\text{He} + \gamma$$

✓*Quick check 1*

Conservation of charge and nucleon number

From the above equations, you can see that:

- charge is conserved (same total of Z's on left and right);
- nucleon (mass) number is conserved (the A's also balance).

Hint

More about mass conservation on pages 52–53.

Fundamental forces

The protons in the nucleus repel each other because of the electrostatic repulsion between their positive charges. The gravitational attraction between them is far too weak to overcome this. They (and the neutrons) are held together by the **strong nuclear force**, one of the four fundamental forces of nature.

The fourth fundamental force is the **weak nuclear force**, which is involved in beta decay.

Examiner tip

You should be able to calculate the electrostatic repulsion between protons using Coulomb's law (page 38) and their gravitational attraction using Newton's law (page 13).

Fundamental particles

Protons and neutrons belong to a family of particles called **hadrons**. These are particles affected by the strong nuclear force. Each hadron is made up of two or three fundamental particles called **quarks**.

Fundamental particles cannot be divided into more fundamental parts. There are two families:

- **Leptons:** This family includes electrons and neutrinos. They do not experience the strong nuclear force.

- **Quarks:** The strong nuclear force acts between quarks. The table shows some properties of three types of quark. Other properties of quarks include charm, topness and bottomness.

Quark (flavour)	Charge Q	Baryon number B	Strangeness S
up (u)	$+2/3\ e$	$+1/3$	0
down (d)	$-1/3\ e$	$+1/3$	0
strange (s)	$-1/3\ e$	$+1/3$	-1

Protons and neutrons are each made up of three quarks:

proton = up, up, down (uud)   **neutron = up, down, down (udd)**

The properties of hadrons can be found by adding up the properties of their quarks.

✔ *Quick check 2 and 3*

Beta decay

In beta-minus decay, a neutron emits an electron and becomes a proton. We can say that a down quark has become an up quark:

$${}_0^1 n \rightarrow {}_1^1 p + {}_{-1}^0 e + \bar{\nu} + \gamma \qquad \text{or} \qquad d \rightarrow u + {}_{-1}^0 e + \bar{\nu} + \gamma$$

In beta-plus decay, an up quark becomes a down quark:

$${}_1^1 p \rightarrow {}_0^1 n + {}_{+1}^0 e + \nu + \gamma \qquad \text{or} \qquad u \rightarrow d + {}_{+1}^0 e + \nu + \gamma$$

✔ *Quick check 4*

Examiner tip

These neutrinos are correctly called 'electron neutrinos', because there are two other types of neutrino, which we will not consider here.

QUICK CHECK QUESTIONS

1 Write equations to represent the following nuclear decays:
   - A polonium nucleus ${}_{84}^{210}$ Po emits an alpha particle and a gamma-photon to become an isotope of lead Pb.
   - A potassium nucleus ${}_{19}^{42}$ K decays by beta emission to become an isotope of calcium Ca. A gamma photon is also emitted.

2 Use the quark model to explain why a proton has charge $+e$ while the neutron has no charge.

3 Determine the values of baryon number B and strangeness S for a proton and for a neutron.

4 Give the names of all the particles produced when an up quark decays to become a down quark.

UNIT 2

Mass–energy conservation

Energy is released during radioactive decay. The particles fly apart (they have kinetic energy), and a gamma photon may be released. Where does this energy come from?

Disappearing mass

In radioactive decay, a nucleus emits one or more particles.

mass of particles before decay > mass of particles after decay

The decrease in mass Δm is accounted for by the appearance of an amount of energy ΔE. Δm and ΔE are related by **Einstein's equation:**

$$\Delta E = \Delta m \times c^2$$

where c is the speed of light in free space, 3.00×10^8 m s^{-1}.

Examiner tip

Most people remember this equation as $E = mc^2$.

■ WORKED EXAMPLE

A neutron decays to become a proton and an electron. How much energy is released? (Values of mass are shown in the table. Inspection shows that the proton and electron together have less mass than the neutron.)

Particle	Mass/kg
Neutron, n	$m_n = 1.674\ 928 \times 10^{-27}$
Proton, p	$m_p = 1.672\ 623 \times 10^{-27}$
Electron, e	$m_e = 0.000\ 911 \times 10^{-27}$

STEP 1 Write down an equation for the reaction:

$$n \rightarrow p + e$$

STEP 2 Calculate the loss in mass Δm:

$$\Delta m = m_n - (m_p + m_e) = 1.394 \times 10^{-30}\ \text{kg}$$

STEP 3 Calculate the energy ΔE released:

$$\Delta E = \Delta m \times c^2 = 1.394 \times 10^{-30}\ \text{kg} \times (3 \times 10^8\ \text{m s}^{-1})^2 = 1.25 \times 10^{-13}\ \text{J}$$

Examiner tip

Note that it is necessary to work to 7 significant figures, because the differences between the quantities are very small. Use your calculator!

✓ *Quick check 1 and 2*

Binding energy, fission and fusion

The nucleons of a nucleus are bound together. Energy is needed to separate them. The **binding energy** of a nucleus is the energy needed to separate a nucleus into its individual nucleons. (It may help to think of this as the *unbinding energy* of the nucleus.) The graph shows the binding energy per nucleon of all nuclei. Iron (Fe) is at the highest point; its nucleons are most tightly bound together.

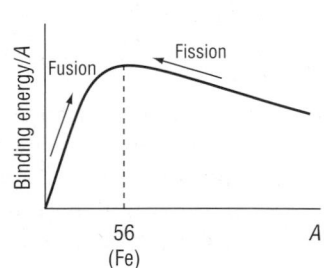

In **nuclear fusion**, small nuclei bind together to form a bigger nucleus. Energy is released; the nucleons are more tightly bound together. High temperatures and pressures are required (as in the core of a star) to overcome the mutual repulsion of the nuclei.

In **nuclear fission**, a large nucleus splits to form two or more smaller nuclei. Again, energy is released; the nucleons are more tightly bound together in the resulting nuclei.

✓ *Quick check 3, 4 and 5*

Fission reactors

In fission, a single neutron causes a large nucleus to split. This is **induced fission**. 2, 3 or 4 neutrons are produced (as well as the smaller daughter nuclei). If, on average, one or more of these neutrons goes on to cause another fission event, we have a **chain reaction**.

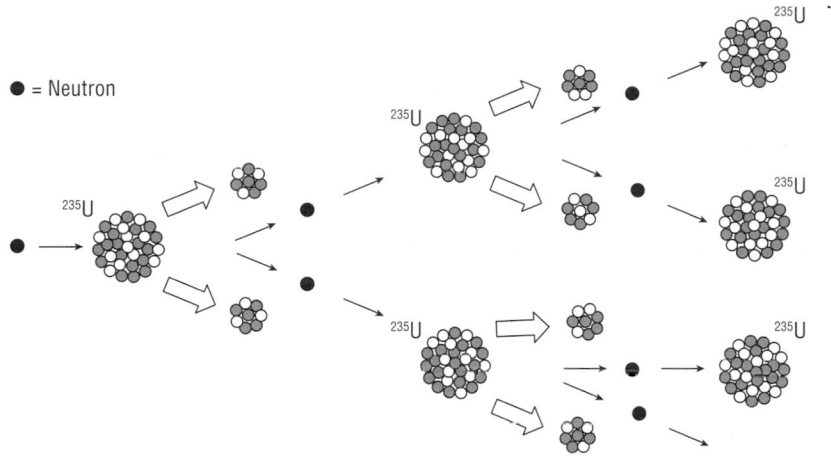

In the reactor **core**, the fuel rods are surrounded by a **moderator** which slows down the neutrons, so that they interact more strongly with nuclei. **Control rods** absorb neutrons strongly, so they can stop the reaction. Coolant carries the heat away to the boiler.

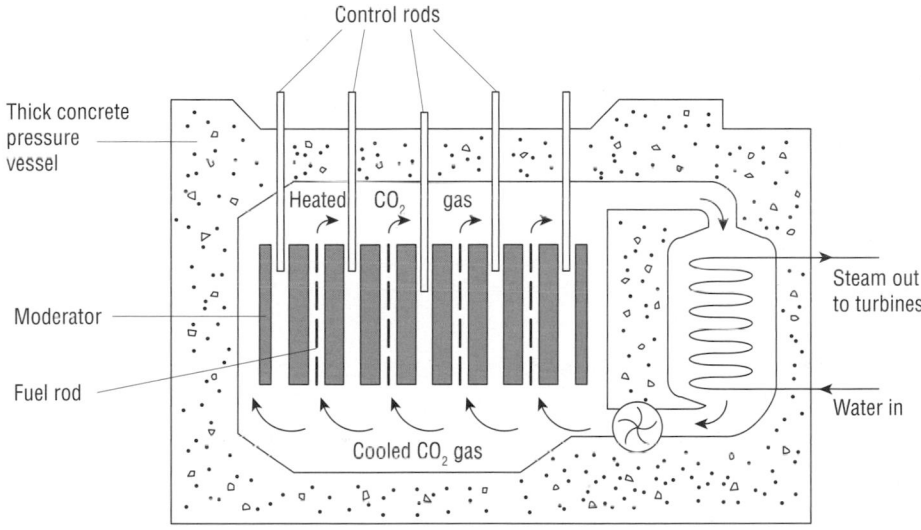

✔ *Quick check 6*

QUICK CHECK QUESTIONS

1. A fast-moving electron may be captured by a proton to form a neutron. However, a stationary electron cannot be captured. Explain why not, using ideas about mass–energy conservation. (You may wish to refer to the table of mass values on the opposite page.)

2. The Sun radiates energy into space at the rate of 4×10^{26} W. By how much does its mass decrease each second? ($c = 3 \times 10^8$ m s^{-1}.)

3. In nuclear fission, a 'mother' nucleus splits to form two 'daughter' nuclei; some neutrons are also released. What can you say about the mass of these products, compared with that of the mother nucleus?

4. The equation below represents a nuclear fission event. Determine x (the number of neutrons released).

   $$^{235}_{92}\text{U} \rightarrow {}^{138}_{54}\text{Xe} + {}^{95}_{38}\text{Sr} + x\,{}^{1}_{0}\text{n}$$

5. The equation below represents a nuclear fusion event. What is particle X?

   $$^{2}_{1}\text{H} + {}^{2}_{1}\text{H} \rightarrow {}^{3}_{1}\text{H} + \text{X}$$

6. Describe briefly how the control rods in a fission reactor core can be used to slow down or speed up a chain reaction.

Radioactive decay

Key words

- activity
- becquerel
- decay constant

It is impossible to predict when an individual nucleus will decay; it occurs spontaneously. As a consequence, the decay of a sample is *random*. If you monitor the decay of a long-lived isotope, you will observe fluctuations in the count rate. Consequently, readings must be averaged.

Ionising radiation

As alpha, beta and gamma radiations pass through matter, they lose energy. Their interactions with matter cause ionisation – electrons are knocked from neutral atoms. Alpha radiation interacts most strongly, so its range is least (a few centimetres in air).

Radiation	Nature	Absorbed by	Range
Alpha, α	Helium nucleus (2 protons + 2 neutrons)	Thin paper	Least
Beta, β	Electron	A few mm of aluminium	
Gamma, γ	Electromagnetic radiation	A few cm of lead	Most

✓*Quick check 1*

Safety precautions in handling, storage and disposal of radioactive materials must take account of these hazards.

- Avoid direct contact with sources.
- Handle solid sources using tongs.
- Keep at a safe distance when working with sources.
- Store sources in lead-lined containers.
- Dispose of sources away from human activity, and in forms that cannot leak.

Activity of a sample

The **activity** *A* of a sample is the average number of nuclei in the sample that decay per second (the average rate of decay).

Units Activity is expressed in **becquerels (Bq)**:

$$1\,\text{Bq} = 1\,\text{s}^{-1}\ (1\text{ decay per second})$$

We have to consider the *average* (or *mean*) number of decays per second, because the rate fluctuates randomly. In practice, it is difficult to detect all the decays that occur, so we may use the measured **count rate**, instead of the activity. The **corrected count rate** takes account of the background count rate.

✓*Quick check 2 and 3*

Decay constant

Some radioactive materials decay very quickly; others decay very slowly. The difference lies in the **decay constant** λ. The decay constant for a particular isotope is the probability that an individual nucleus will decay in unit time.

Units s^{-1} (or day^{-1}, or year^{-1}, etc.)

For example, suppose an isotope has a decay constant $\lambda = 0.1$ year^{-1}. If we could observe a single nucleus of this isotope for 1 year, there is a probability of 0.1 (i.e. 1 in 10) that it will decay in this time. If we could observe 100 of these nuclei for a year, we would expect roughly 10 to decay.

Hence, the activity A of a sample depends on two things:

- The decay constant λ of the isotope.
- The number of undecayed nuclei N it contains.

activity = decay constant × number of undecayed nuclei $A = \lambda N$

$\checkmark$ *Quick check 4, 5 and 6*

> ## ■ WORKED EXAMPLE
>
> A sample of radioactive carbon contains 2×10^{13} undecayed carbon nuclei. The decay constant for this isotope is 4×10^{-12} s^{-1}. What is the activity of the sample?
>
> Substituting in the equation gives
>
> $A = \lambda N = 4 \times 10^{-12}$ s^{-1} $\times 2 \times 10^{13} = 80$ s^{-1}
>
> So the activity is 80 s^{-1}, or 80 Bq.

Module 3

QUICK CHECK QUESTIONS

1 Of the three types of ionising radiation considered here (α, β and γ), which interacts least strongly with matter as it passes through it?

2 In a particular sample of a radioactive substance, 12 000 nuclei decay on average each minute. Calculate the sample's activity.

3 A Geiger counter placed next to a sample of a radioactive material detects an average of 1.5 counts per second. Give two reasons why it would be incorrect to conclude that the sample's activity is 1.5 Bq.

4 A radioactive isotope has a decay constant of 0.25×10^{-3} s^{-1}. Calculate the activity of a sample which contains 2.5×10^6 undecayed nuclei.

5 A sample of a radioactive isotope contains 5×10^8 undecayed nuclei. Its activity is 600 Bq. What is the decay constant for this isotope?

6 A sample contains a radioactive nuclide of decay constant 0.004 s^{1}. Its activity is determined to be 280 s^{-1}. How many undecayed nuclei does it contain?

Radioactive decay equations

The decay of a radioactive substance is like the discharge of a capacitor: both follow an exponential pattern. The rate of decay depends on the **half-life** of the radioactive substance. The half-life is related to the decay constant.

The pattern of decay

As a sample of a radioactive substance decays, several quantities follow the same pattern:

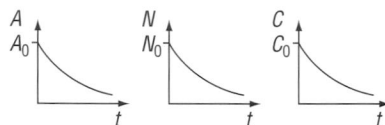

- A, the activity of the sample.
- N, the number of undecayed nuclei.
- C, the corrected count rate.

Each of these quantities starts at a certain initial value (e.g. A_0); its value falls rapidly at first, then more and more slowly. This is an **exponential decay**.

In practice, because radioactive decay is random and spontaneous, an experimental curve will have points scattered about the smooth theoretical curve. Furthermore, a true exponential curve never reaches zero. However, in the case of radioactivity, the last undecayed nucleus may eventually decay, and the curve will reach zero.

✓ *Quick check 1*

The decay equation

Each of the quantities above follows an equation of the same form:

$$x = x_0 e^{-\lambda t}$$

For example, activity A varies as $A = A_0 e^{-\lambda t}$. (Note the similarity to the equations for capacitor discharge, page 46).

✓ *Quick check 2*

■ WORKED EXAMPLE

A sample of a radioactive nuclide initially consists of 3×10^6 undecayed nuclei. How many will remain undecayed after 1 hour? The decay constant, λ, for this nuclide is 10^{-3} s^{-1}.

STEP 1 Write down what you know, and what you want to know:
$N_0 = 3 \times 10^6$, $\lambda = 10^{-3}$ s^{-1}, $t = 1$, h $= 3600$ s, $N = ?$

STEP 2 Write down the appropriate form of the decay equation:
$N = N_0 e^{-\lambda t}$

STEP 3 Substitute and solve, calculating the value of $-\lambda t$ first:
$N = 3 \times 10^6 \exp(-10^{-3}$ s$^{-1} \times 3600$ s$) = 3 \times 10^6 \exp(-3.6) = 82\,000$

You should be able to complete this calculation without writing down the intermediate step. Note that the answer is given to 2 significant figures; because of the randomness of radioactive decay, we cannot say that 81971 nuclei will remain after 1 hour.

✓ *Quick check 3*

Half-life and decay constant

The **half-life, $t_{1/2}$,** of a radioactive nuclide is the mean (average) time for the number of nuclei of that nuclide to decay to half of its original value.

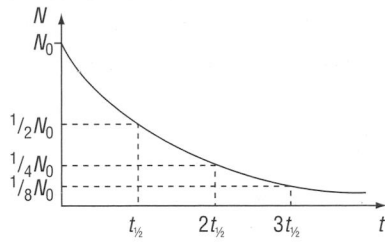

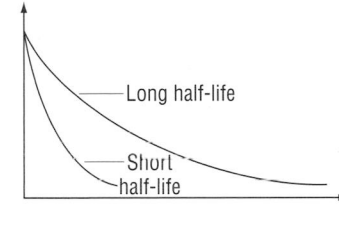

We have to say *mean time* since every measurement will give a slightly different value, because of random fluctuations.

The smaller the decay constant λ, the longer the half-life $t_{1/2}$. These two quantities are related by

$$\lambda t_{1/2} = 0.693$$

✔ *Quick check 4 and 5*

Radiocarbon dating

Living material contains carbon, a tiny fraction of which is the radioisotope carbon-14. After a living organism dies, the fraction of C-14 present gradually decays. By measuring the fraction remaining, the time since death can be found.

Since the half-life of C-14 is 5730 years, ages of a few hundred or a few thousand years can be determined with reasonable accuracy.

✔ *Quick check 6*

QUICK CHECK QUESTIONS

1   Use the equation $A = \lambda N$ to explain why the activity A of a radioactive nuclide follows the same pattern of decay as the number of undecayed nuclei N.

2   Write down an exponential decay equation to represent how the corrected count rate C decreases with time t.

3   A particular radioactive nuclide has decay constant 0.03 year^{-1}. A sample has initial activity 40 Bq. What will its activity be after 5 years?

4   Radioactive carbon-14 has a half-life of 5730 years. What is the decay constant for this isotope?

5   Nuclide X has decay constant 6×10^{-3} s^{-1}. What is its half-life? What fraction of a sample of this nuclide will remain after 200 s?

6   Use your answer to question 4 to determine the fraction of C-14 which remains in a sample of organic material 100 years after death, and 100 000 years after death. Explain why these ages cannot be accurately determined by radiocarbon dating.

X-rays

Key words

- X-rays
- photoelectric effect
- Compton scattering
- pair production
- intensity
- attenuation
- contrast

X-rays are a vital tool in medicine because they can show up internal structures of the body.

How X-rays are produced

X-rays are short-wavelength electromagnetic waves. They are effectively the same as gamma rays, the difference being in how they are produced. X-rays are produced when fast-moving electrons are suddenly decelerated; gamma rays are produced by radioactive substances. The diagram shows the principles of X-ray production in an X-ray tube.

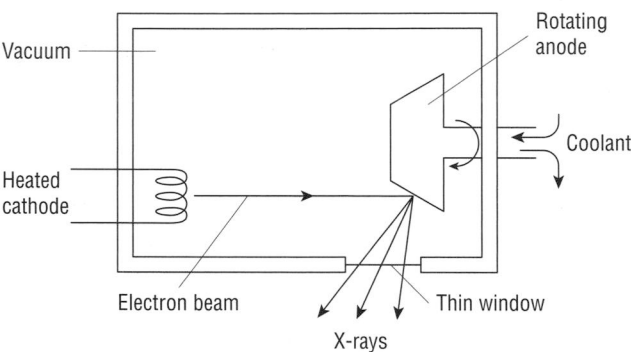

- There is a high voltage (kilovolts, kV) between the metal anode (+) and the heated filament or cathode (–).
- Electrons leave the filament by thermionic emission and accelerate towards the anode, or target, which is made of a dense metal such as tungsten that readily absorbs electrons.
- They are stopped by the anode, and a fraction of their energy appears as X-rays.
- Most of the electrons' energy appears as heat in the anode, which must be cooled.
- A metal tube outside the window collimates the X-rays to form a narrow beam.

✔ *Quick check 1*

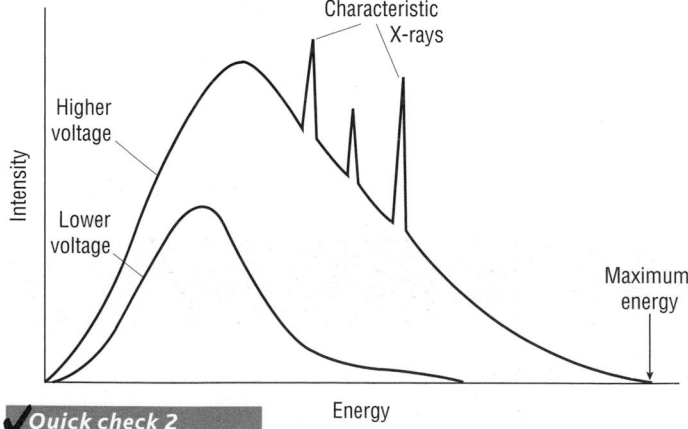

X-ray spectra

The fast-moving electrons lose their energy as they interact with the electrons in the metal anode. A typical spectrum shows two main features:

- The bulk of the X-rays arise when an electron loses its energy in multiple interactions, producing several X-rays.
- A few *characteristic X-rays* arise when electrons change energy levels in atoms of the anode; their frequencies are characteristic of the metal.

✔ *Quick check 2*

Examiner tip

You should be familiar with the photoelectric effect for light (AS Unit 2 Module 5, page 66 of the Revision Guide).

X-ray absorption mechanisms

In medicine, we make use of the fact that X-rays are absorbed to different degrees by different materials. There are three important mechanisms of absorption:

- In the **photoelectric effect**, an X-ray is absorbed when it strikes an atomic electron, transferring its energy to the electron, which escapes its atom.

- In **Compton scattering**, an X-ray transfers some of its energy to an atomic electron; the remaining energy appears as an X-ray photon, travelling in a different direction.

- In **pair production**, an X-ray strikes an atomic nucleus, producing an electron–positron pair.

An X-ray tube is typically operated at 30 kV; this gives X-rays which are of low enough energy to be absorbed by bone. There is less absorption by flesh, so there is good **contrast** between flesh and bone. The dominant absorption process is the photoelectric effect. (Higher-energy X-rays would be more penetrating, i.e. they would be less absorbed.)

✔ *Quick check 3*

X-ray intensity and attenuation

The intensity I of radiation is the power per unit cross-sectional area.

The intensity of X-rays decreases as they pass through a medium; they are **attenuated** according to the equation

$$I = I_0\, e^{-\mu x}$$

where μ is the **attenuation coefficient** and x is the thickness of the medium.

Examiner tip

Intensity was defined and discussed in Unit 2 Module 4 (page 57) of the AS Revision Guide.

✔ *Quick check 4 and 5*

Practical X-ray techniques

Contrast media are substances such as barium and iodine, used because they are good absorbers of X-rays. In a barium meal, the patient swallows a barium-containing liquid which shows up the stomach and other soft tissues.

Image intensifiers are electronic devices which convert weak X-rays into brighter light.

A **computerised axial tomography (CAT) scanner** takes X-rays of the patient from many different angles and then constructs images of slices through their body.

Advantages of CAT scans over conventional X-rays:

- Give 3D images, including precise positions of structures.

- Show up small differences in tissue density.

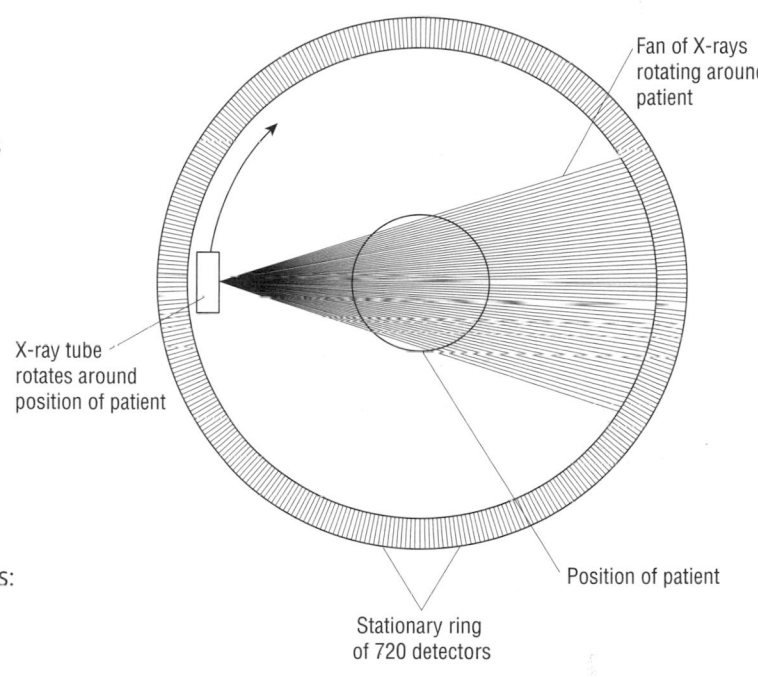

Fan of X-rays rotating around patient

X-ray tube rotates around position of patient

Position of patient

Stationary ring of 720 detectors

✔ *Quick check 6*

Module 4

QUICK CHECK QUESTIONS

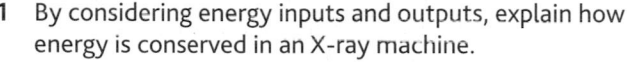

1 By considering energy inputs and outputs, explain how energy is conserved in an X-ray machine.

2 Describe how the principal features of an X-ray spectrum change as the voltage between the anode and the cathode is increased.

3 (a) If the voltage of an X-ray tube is increased, the X-rays become more penetrating. Explain how this will affect the brightness of the image produced.

   (b) At higher voltages, there may be less contrast in the X-ray image. Explain the term *contrast*.

4 What are the units of intensity?

5 The attenuation coefficient for flesh has an approximate value of 0.07 cm^{-1}. Calculate the fractional decrease in intensity of an X-ray beam after it has passed through 20 cm of flesh.

6 Explain why a contrast medium such as barium is needed when imaging soft tissue such as the intestines.

UNIT 2

Diagnostic methods in medicine

Key words
- radioactive tracer
- positron
- Larmor frequency
- relaxation

✓*Quick check 1*

✓*Quick check 2*

✓*Quick check 3*

Radioactivity, magnetic resonance, sound and ultrasound are all used in techniques of non-invasive diagnosis, avoiding the need to cut open the patient.

Radioactive tracers and the gamma camera

Technetium-99m is a metastable radioisotope with a half-life of 6 hours. A patient is injected with a compound containing Tc-99m; this **tracer** appears in the organ of interest. The gamma radiation it emits is detected from outside the body.

In a **gamma camera**, a patient is injected with a radioactive tracer. Radiation is collected by the camera, outside the body, to give an image of areas where the tracer has accumulated.

Positron emission tomography (PET)

In a PET scan, the radioactive substance used is a **positron** emitter. Each positron, when it is emitted, annihilates with an electron. Their energy is released as two gamma photons with equal energies and travelling in opposite directions. These are detected and the site of emission deduced.

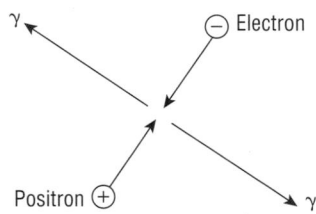

PET scanning gives three-dimensional images of the patient's internal organs. It is used, for example, to show where glucose is being consumed in metabolic activity.

Magnetic resonance

Magnetic resonance imaging (MRI) is a non-invasive imaging technique which does not rely on ionising radiation. It can produce images of slices through the patient's body. It is mostly used to detect the nuclei of hydrogen atoms (found in water and most biochemical substances).

Nuclear magnetic resonance works like this:

- Nuclei spin about an axis, rather like a spinning top.

- In a magnetic field B, the nuclei line up; the axis of spin precesses about the magnetic field direction with a frequency (called the **Larmor frequency**) which is proportional to B.

- Because the Larmor frequency is in the radio frequency (RF) range, radio waves of the same frequency can be used to flip the nuclei from a low energy state to a high energy state. This is **magnetic resonance**.

- When a nucleus has flipped up to the higher energy state, it **relaxes** back to the lower energy state, emitting energy as it does so. It is this energy which is detected in MRI.

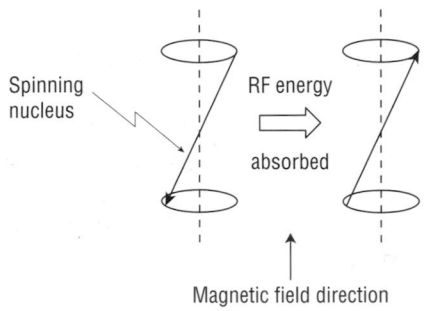

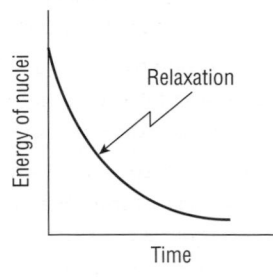

Magnetic resonance imaging

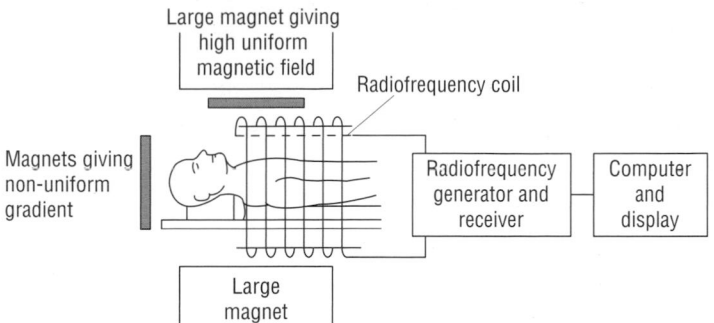

- The patient lies in the field of a powerful electromagnet. This field aligns the nuclei in the patient's tissues.

- The gradient coils produce the gradient field which varies gradually along the patient's body.

- The RF coils transmit pulses of RF radiation into the body. Because of the gradient field, only nuclei in a thin slice of the patient's body will resonate and absorb energy.

- The second set of RF coils detect the radio waves emitted by relaxing nuclei.

- The detected signal is analysed by computer.

Distinguishing tissues

MRI detects radiation from relaxing hydrogen nuclei (protons). These nuclei relax more quickly in fatty tissues than in watery tissues. Hence the rate at which RF radiation is emitted by the tissue indicates its nature, and a picture of the tissues can be built up.

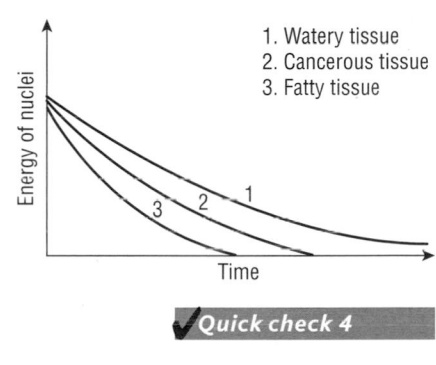

✔ *Quick check 4*

Advantages of MRI	Disadvantages of MRI
Does not use ionising radiation, which is a hazard to patient and medical staff.	Can interfere with medical implants, e.g. heart pacemakers, surgical pins
Gives clearer contrast between different soft tissues than X-ray scans.	Not as good as X-rays for imaging bones.
The computer can generate images of slices or pseudo-three-dimensional images.	Screening of external RF fields is required.
Patient does not feel anything; no side effects.	Gradient coil system is noisy and claustrophobic.

✔ *Quick check 5*

QUICK CHECK QUESTIONS

1. **(a)** Why is 6 hours an appropriate half-life for a radioactive tracer?
   (b) Why should a radioactive tracer be a gamma emitter?

2. In PET scanning, two gamma rays are emitted. If one of a pair is detected slightly earlier than the other, what can you say about the site at which they were produced?

3. In nuclear magnetic resonance:
   (a) How does the Larmor frequency change if the magnetic field is increased?
   (b) Why is the process by which nuclei absorb energy described as *resonance*?

4. In MRI:
   (a) Which coil provides the strong, steady magnetic field?
   (b) What is the function of the gradient coils?
   (c) Why are there two sets of RF coils?

5. A patient has apparently broken some ribs, and there may be damage to their lungs. Explain why it might be advantageous to make both an MRI scan and a CAT scan of the patient's chest.

Ultrasound in medicine

Key words

- piezoelectric effect
- ultrasound transducer
- acoustic impedance
- Doppler effect

Ultrasound waves are, in effect, sound waves with frequencies beyond the range of human hearing, i.e. above 20 kHz. They are longitudinal mechanical waves, and have several uses in medicine.

Producing ultrasound

Ultrasound is produced and detected by means of the **piezoelectric effect**, a phenomenon shown by certain crystals:

- When a voltage is applied across the crystal, it contracts. Removing the voltage causes it to relax to its original dimensions.

- When a stress is applied to the crystal, causing it to contract, a voltage appears across the crystal. Removing the stress causes the voltage to disappear.

An **ultrasound transducer** can both produce and detect ultrasound.

- A varying voltage is applied to a crystal, causing it to contract and relax at the applied frequency. This generates ultrasound waves.

- Alternatively, if ultrasound waves strike the crystal, the varying stress results in a voltage which varies with the frequency of the ultrasound.

✓*Quick check 1*

Reflection and refraction

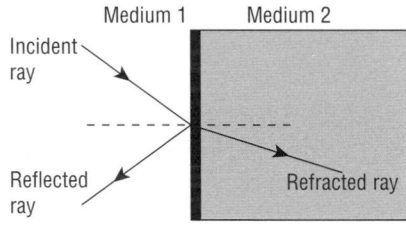

When an ultrasound wave strikes the boundary between two media, it is partly reflected and partly refracted.

The greater the difference in **acoustic impedance Z** between the two materials, the greater the fraction reflected.

Examiner tip

A similar diagram can be drawn for a light ray passing from one medium to another.

Acoustic impedance = density × speed of sound $Z = \rho c$

Ultrasound scanning uses the fact that different materials have different values of Z.

Material	Acoustic impedance/10^3 kg m^{-2} s^{-1}
air	0.4
water	1500
bone	7800
soft tissue	1600
blood	1600
fatty tissue	1400

✓*Quick check 2*

Calculating the fraction reflected

An ultrasound wave incident on a boundary between two media **1** and **2** has intensity I_0; the reflected wave has intensity I_r. The fraction reflected depends on the acoustic impedances of the two media, Z_1 and Z_2:

$$I_r/I_0 = (Z_2 - Z_1)^2/(Z_2 + Z_1)^2$$

From the table opposite, you can see that:
- Bone and tissue have very different values of Z, so roughly half of the ultrasound is reflected at the boundary.
- Tissues such as fat and muscle have very similar values of Z, so there is little reflection.
- Air has a very low value of Z, so almost all ultrasound is reflected at an air–tissue boundary. To avoid this, the patient's skin must be smeared with a gel to allow the ultrasound to enter the body (impedance matching).

✓*Quick check 3 and 4*

Types of ultrasound scan

You can think of ultrasound scanning as being similar to the way in which radar detects aircraft, or sonar detects shoals of fish in the sea. The time taken for the echo (reflected waves) to return can be used to calculate the distance to the reflecting surface.
- In an **A scan**, ultrasound waves are sent into the body. Reflected waves are detected coming from boundaries between different materials. The time taken for the echo to return is used to calculate the depth of each boundary.
- A **B scan** is more complex. The ultrasound transducer is scanned across the patient; a picture is built up on a screen from the A scan results at each point.

✓*Quick check 5*

Doppler ultrasound

This is a technique used to determine the speed of blood. It depends on the **Doppler effect**:
- When waves are reflected by a stationary object, their frequency is unchanged.
- When they are reflected by an object moving away from their source, their frequency decreases.
- For an object moving towards the source, the reflected waves have an increased frequency.

To measure the speed of blood flow:
- Ultrasound waves of known frequency are directed at a blood vessel.
- Reflected waves are detected and their frequency measured by comparison with the initial waves.
- The greater the change in frequency, the faster the blood cells must be moving.

✓*Quick check6*

Module 4

QUICK CHECK QUESTIONS

1 Explain how a piezoelectric transducer can both produce and detect ultrasound waves.

2 Calculate the acoustic impedance of soft bone (density = 1300 kg m⁻³, speed of sound = 2800 m s⁻¹).

3 Ultrasound waves are incident on a muscle–bone boundary. If the fraction reflected is 0.42, what fraction is refracted?

4 Calculate the fraction of ultrasound refracted when ultrasound waves strike a boundary between blood and fatty tissue (use values of Z from the table opposite).

5 An ultrasound scan (type B) can take several seconds to perform. Explain why the image of a patient's heart may be blurred as a result.

6 As the heart beats, the rate at which blood flows varies. How would this show up in a Doppler ultrasound measurement?

UNIT 2

The structure of the universe

Key words

- stellar evolution
- Olbers' paradox
- cosmological principle

The **universe** consists of all the matter and energy which we can detect or which we might be able to detect. There are billions of **galaxies** in the universe; each galaxy is made up of billions of stars.

The solar system

The **solar system** consists of the Sun (a star) and all the objects which orbit it, held in their orbits by its gravitational pull: planets, planetary satellites (e.g. the Earth's Moon), comets, asteroids, etc.

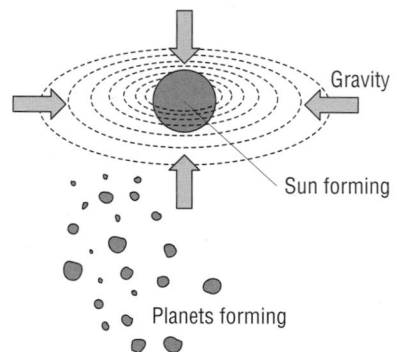

The solar system formed from the contraction of a diffuse cloud of interstellar dust and gas under the pull of its own gravity.

- Most of the mass (largely hydrogen gas) contracted to form the Sun, heating up as its potential energy decreased.

- A tiny fraction of the mass formed the planets.

✓Quick check 1

Life of a star

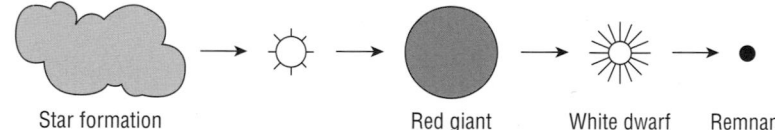

The Sun is roughly halfway through its life. It releases energy through the process of nuclear fusion.

- Towards the end of its life, it will probably swell up to become a **red giant** (cooler and much larger than at present).

- Then it will shed outer layers of gas. The core will contract to form a hot **white dwarf** star.

- Eventually, this will fade away.

A star which is considerably more massive than the Sun would behave differently:

- After becoming a super red giant, its core collapses and then explodes outwards as a supernova.

- The very dense remnant is either a **neutron star** or (if it is massive enough) a **black hole**.

✓Quick check 2

Hint

Refer back to page 52 for a reminder of nuclear fusion.

Module 5

The scale of the universe

Astronomers use a number of different units to measure distances in the solar system and in the universe.

Examiner tip

You should learn the SI equivalents of 1 light-year and 1 parsec, shown in the table on this page.

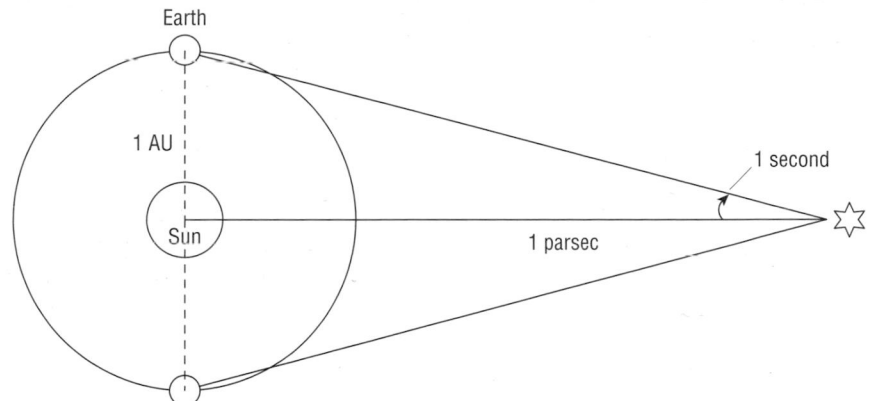

Unit name and symbol	Definition	Approximate value
Astronomical unit (AU)	Average distance between Earth and Sun	~1.5×10^{11} m
Light-year (ly)	Distance travelled by light in 1 year in free space	~9×10^{15} m
Parsec (pc)	Distance of object whose parallax is 2 seconds – see diagram	~3×10^{16} m; 3.26 ly

✓ *Quick check 3 and 4*

Olbers' paradox and the Cosmological Principle

Newton suggested that the universe was infinitely large, with stars distributed throughout and stationary. Olbers pointed out that it is dark at night; Newton must be wrong, because his model suggests that, in whichever direction we look, there would be a star and hence light.

We can conclude that:
- either the universe is not infinite
- or the stars are not uniformly distributed
- or it is not static

(or two or all of these might be true).

Today, it is generally accepted that the universe is not infinite, and that it is expanding rather than static.

The Cosmological Principle states that the universe has a generally uniform appearance. On a large scale, regions close to us are similar to the most distant regions. This is an assumption which we must make if we are to deduce the nature of the universe from 'local' observations and measurements.

Hint

The evidence that the universe is expanding appears on pages 66–69.

✓ *Quick check 5*

Module 5

QUICK CHECK QUESTIONS

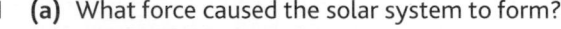

1 (a) What force caused the solar system to form?
   (b) What did it form from?
   (c) Why did the material which formed the Sun become hot?

2 (a) List the sequence of stages through which the Sun will pass in its lifetime.
   (b) How would this sequence differ if the Sun was ten times as massive?

3 The speed of light in free space is 3×10^8 m s^{-1}; 1 year is ~3.1×10^7 s. What is 1 light-year in km?

4 Star A has a parallax of 0.04 seconds of arc. Star B has a parallax of 0.02 seconds of arc.
   (a) Which star is more distant from the Sun?
   (b) What is the distance to star A from the Sun, in parsecs?

5 Why is it important that the Cosmological Principle should be true?

UNIT 2

The expanding universe

Edwin Hubble discovered that the universe is expanding. This conclusion was based on measurements of the redshift of light from distant galaxies.

Understanding redshift

Stationary source

Observer

λ

λ + Δλ

Receding source

Examiner tip

Recall from Unit 2 in AS Physics that isolated atoms give line spectra.

When a star, galaxy or other light source is moving away from the observer, its light is redshifted. That is, there is an increase in the wavelengths of lines in its spectrum, so that the lines appear to have moved towards the red end of the spectrum.

This is an example of the Doppler effect. For a spectral line of wavelength λ, the change in wavelength (the redshift) $\Delta\lambda$ depends on the speed v at which the source is receding. The greater the speed, the greater the redshift:

$$\Delta\lambda / \lambda = v/c$$

where c is the speed of light in free space. So measurements of $\Delta\lambda$ allow the speed of recession of a galaxy to be determined.

Examiner tip

The entire calculation could be carried out in nm, to avoid including the factor of 10^{-9}.

✓ *Quick check 1, 2 and 3*

■ WORKED EXAMPLE

A star is receding from the Earth with a speed of 0.024c. Calculate the redshift in light of wavelength 550 nm. What will be the wavelength of this light?

STEP 1 Calculate $\Delta\lambda$:
$$\Delta\lambda = \lambda \times v/c = 550 \times 10^{-9} \times 0.024 = 13.2 \times 10^{-9} \text{ m}$$
STEP 2 Calculate the new wavelength. Note that the wavelength is *increased* for a redshift.
$$\lambda = 550 + 13.2 = 563.2 \text{ nm}$$

Hubble's results

Hubble also had to measure the distances of the galaxies he observed. He did this by observing the brightness of a standard type of star, the Cepheid variables. He found that a graph of speed against distance was a straight line through the origin. This indicated that the speed of recession is proportional to distance.

Velocity of recession, v

Distance of galaxy, x

This is **Hubble's law**:

speed of recession ∝ distance $v = H_0 x$

where H_0 is the Hubble constant. Hubble concluded that the universe is expanding – everything is moving away from everything else, not just moving away from the Earth.

✔ *Quick check 4*

The age of the universe

All of the galaxies in the universe are moving away from each other. We can imagine reversing this picture; in the past, the galaxies were all much closer together and, at some time, they were all compressed together in a tiny space. This suggests that the universe began from a single point, billions of years ago. We can deduce the age of the universe from the Hubble constant H_0:

age of universe ≈ $1/H_0$

Measurements of H_0 are difficult, so the value is uncertain. A good estimate is:

$H_0 = 71$ km s^{-1} Mpc^{-1}

Since 1 Mpc (megaparsec) is ~3×10^{22} m, this gives

$$H_0 = \frac{71\,000 \text{ m s}^{-1}}{3 \times 10^{22} \text{ m}} = 2.4 \times 10^{-18} \text{ s}^{-1}$$

$$\text{age of universe} = \frac{1}{2.4 \times 10^{-18} \text{ s}^{-1}} = 4.2 \times 10^{17} \text{ s} = 13.4 \times 10^9 \text{ years}$$

So the universe is apparently about 13 billion years old.

> **Examiner tip**
>
> You need to be able to convert H_0 from units of km s^{-1} Mpc^{-1} to s^{-1}, as shown here. It helps to include the units in the conversion.

✔ *Quick check 5*

Hubble's law and Olbers' paradox

Hubble's law clearly shows that the universe is not static; it is expanding. This can help to explain Olbers' ideas.

Hubble showed that distant galaxies are moving very fast. Very distant galaxies will have large redshifts, so that their light will be shifted out of the visible region of the spectrum, and hence they will not contribute to the light in our sky. This is one of the reasons why it is dark at night.

Module 5

QUICK CHECK QUESTIONS

1 What can we deduce if the light from a star is blue-shifted?

2 A distant galaxy has a fractional redshift $\Delta\lambda/\lambda$ of 0.13. Calculate its velocity of recession.

3 A star is moving away from the Earth with a velocity of 0.50×10^8 m s^{-1}. What will be the redshift $\Delta\lambda$ of a line in its spectrum whose frequency is 4×10^{14} Hz?

> **Examiner tip**
>
> You will have to use the equation $v = f\lambda$ to deduce the wavelength of the light. $c = 3.0 \times 10^8$ m s^{-1}.

4 How would Hubble's graph of speed against distance change if the most distant galaxies were moving more slowly than suggested by his measurements?

5 The Chandra satellite was used to make measurements which gave a value for the Hubble constant of $H_0 = 77$ km s^{-1} Mpc^{-1}. This suggests that the universe is expanding faster than previously thought.
   (a) Does this suggest that the universe is older or younger than previously thought?
   (b) Use this value of H_0 to deduce a value for the age of the universe.

The evolution of the universe

Hubble's work was the first indication that the universe started from a big bang. Further evidence that this was a 'hot big bang' comes from the existence of microwave background radiation and the chemical composition of the universe.

The hot big bang model

This model suggests that the universe started from a hot big bang; at some time in the past (approximately 13 billion years ago), all of the matter and energy in today's universe was compressed into a single point, from which it expanded outwards. This implies that the universe is not static, and that it has a finite age, contradicting Newton's ideas (page 65).

The cosmic microwave background radiation

Observations show that, in all directions, we receive **background radiation** whose wavelengths are in the microwave region of the electromagnetic spectrum. The spectrum of this radiation shows that it is similar to that of a black body at a temperature of approximately 3 K (more accurately, 2.73 K).

This radiation is the remnant of the heat radiation which was spread throughout the universe shortly (approx 10^5 years) after the big bang. Because the universe has expanded, the waves have been stretched; their wavelengths have increased, corresponding to a drop in temperature.

✔ *Quick check 1*

Universal evolution

The **hot big bang theory** describes how the universe has changed from a time of 10^{-43} s after the big bang until now, and it predicts how the universe will continue to evolve.

Time from big bang/s	Temperature/K	Dimensions of universe/m	State of universe
10^{-43}–10^{-6}	> 10^{12}	< 10^3	'Sea' of quarks and leptons
10^{-6}–10^2	Falling to 10^7	Growing to 10^{10}	Quarks combining to form hadrons
10^2–10^{13}	Falling to 10^5	Growing to 10^{21}	Nuclei forming; plasma of H, He nuclei, electrons, photons
10^{13} = 500 000 years	10^3	10^{22}	Matter and radiation separate; origin of background radiation
10^{13}–5×10^{17} (present)	Falling to 3 K	10^{26}	Atoms forming, gravity causes stars and planets to form, microwave background cooling

✔ *Quick check 2 and 3*

Possible futures

The universe is expanding. Gravity pulls back on the separating galaxies, tending to make them decelerate.

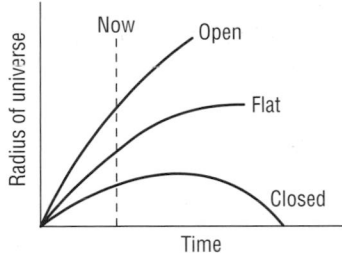

- If gravity is strong enough, the galaxies will eventually reverse their direction of travel and fall back towards a **big crunch**. This is a **closed universe**.
- If gravity is insufficiently strong, the universe will continue to expand for ever. This is an **open universe**.
- The in-between state, where the universe expands more and more slowly but not quite slowly enough to go into reverse is called a **flat universe**.

✓*Quick check 4*

Critical density

Which of these possible futures is correct depends on the density ρ of the universe. The denser the universe, the stronger the pull of gravity and hence the more likely it is that the universe will start to contract. The **critical density** ρ_0 is the density which corresponds to a flat universe.

The critical density is related to the Hubble constant H_0 and to the gravitational constant G:

$$\rho_0 = 3H_0^2/8\pi G$$
$$\rho_0 = 3 \times (2.4 \times 10^{-18})^2/8 \times \pi \times 6.67 \times 10^{-11} \sim 10^{-26}\ \text{kg m}^{-3}$$

This corresponds to about 1 hydrogen atom per cubic metre of the universe.

Measurements suggest that the density of the universe is close to this critical value. Many theoreticians think that it may well be exactly equal to this value – that, unlikely as it seems, we live in a universe with a 'flat' cosmology.

✓*Quick check 5 and 6*

Module 5

QUICK CHECK QUESTIONS

1 Explain how **(a)** the temperature of the microwave background radiation and **(b)** the wavelengths of the radiation will change in the future.

2 What particles were present in the universe in the first microsecond after the big bang?

3 The following were not present immediately after the big bang. In what order did they form?
   stars
   protons
   atomic nuclei
   neutral atoms.

4 What produces the force of gravitation which acts to slow down receding galaxies?

5 If, in a different universe, the force of gravity was much stronger (G greater), would its critical density be greater or less than in our universe?

6 **(a)** If the density of the universe is less than the critical density ρ_0, what will be its fate?
   (b) And if its density is greater than ρ_0?

End-of-unit questions

See Appendix 3 on page 78 for data and formulae provided in the examination.

Module 1: Electric and magnetic fields

1 The diagram shows the electric field between two positively charged metal spheres.

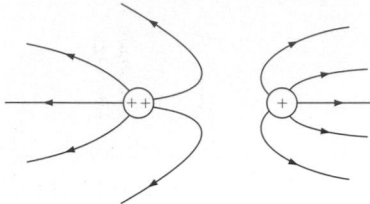

(a) Explain how a diagram of this sort represents the direction of the electric field at a point, and the strength of the field.

(b) Add arrows to the diagram to show the electric force each sphere exerts on the other. What can you say about the magnitudes and directions of these two forces?

2 Two parallel plates, 10 cm apart, are connected to a 2 kV power supply. A dust particle with positive charge 1×10^{-15} C is midway between them.

(a) Draw a diagram to represent the electric field between the plates.

(b) Calculate the electric field strength in the gap between the plates.

(c) Calculate the electric force on the dust particle.

(d) If the particle moves 3 cm closer to the positively charged plate, what can you say about the electric force on it?

3 In an electrostatic dust filter for a workshop, charged dust particles pass through a uniform electric field between metal plates and are deflected onto one of the plates.

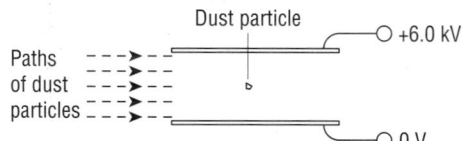

The figure shows a dust particle of mass 400×10^{-15} kg and charge $+1.0 \times 10^{-16}$ C entering the electric field at right angles.

The potential difference across the plates is 6.0 kV and they are 12 mm apart.

(a) Calculate

    (i) the electric field strength in the region between the plates.

    (ii) the force on the dust particle.

    (iii) the acceleration of the dust particle in the direction of this force.

(b) Copy the figure and draw an arrow on the dust particle to show the direction of the force on the dust particle.

(c) Explain why the path taken by the dust particle is not part of a circle.

4 The flux density of a magnetic field can be found by measuring the force on a current-carrying conductor placed in the field. In such a measurement, a 20 cm length of conductor carrying a current of 1.5 A is placed in a field; the greatest force acting on the conductor is found to be 0.06 N.

(a) Draw a diagram to show the relative orientations of the conductor and the magnetic field when the force has its maximum value.

(b) Calculate the flux density of the field.

(c) The conductor is then turned through an angle of 60°. Calculate the force that now acts on it.

5 The diagram shows a coil of 100 turns of wire, placed so that its plane is perpendicular to a horizontal magnetic field of flux density 0.05 T. The coil is rectangular, with sides of lengths 6 cm and 10 cm.

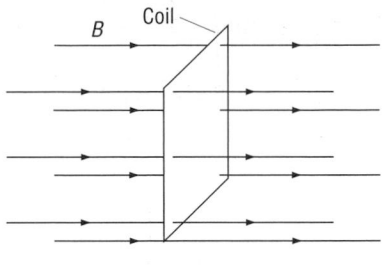

(a) Calculate the flux passing through the coil, and its flux linkage.
(b) The coil is slowly moved downwards through the field, so that its plane remains perpendicular to the flux. Explain why no e.m.f. is induced between its ends.
(c) How could the coil be moved to induce an e.m.f.?

Module 2: Capacitors and exponential decay

6 A 10 μF capacitor is charged to 400 V.
(a) Calculate the charge stored by the capacitor.
(b) Calculate the energy it stores.
The capacitor is disconnected from the source of p.d., and connected to an identical, uncharged capacitor. The charge stored by the capacitor is now shared between the two.
(c) Are the capacitors connected in series or in parallel? Calculate their combined capacitance.
(d) Calculate the p.d. across each of the capacitors.
(e) Calculate the energy stored by each capacitor. What fraction of the energy stored by the single capacitor is this?

7 A 2000 μF capacitor is charged up until the p.d. between its plates is 100 V. It is then allowed to discharge through a 500 kΩ resistor.
(a) Calculate the initial current that flows through the resistor.
(b) Sketch a graph to show how the current through the resistor changes.
(c) Calculate the time constant for the circuit.
(d) Write down an equation to represent how I depends on time t.
(e) Calculate the current flowing through the resistor after 500 s.

8 The graph shows how the charge on a 4.0 μF capacitor changes with time as the capacitor is discharged through a resistor.

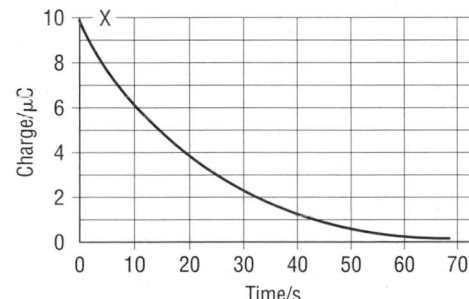

(a) Use the value of the initial charge on the capacitor to calculate the initial voltage across the capacitor.

(b) Estimate the initial discharging current. To do this, draw a tangent to the curve at X. The slope of this tangent gives the initial discharging current.

(c) Using your answers to **a** and **b**, determine the resistance of the resistor.

Module 3: Nuclear physics

9 The atomic nucleus was discovered in a historic experiment devised by Ernest Rutherford. Alpha radiation was directed at a gold foil.

(a) Why were the radiation source, foil and detector in an evacuated chamber?

(b) Summarise the observations made.

(c) Explain why these observations suggested the existence of the nucleus.

(d) Draw a diagram showing typical paths of alpha particles directed towards a gold nucleus.

10 The graph shows how the binding energy per nucleon depends on atomic number for different nuclei. Use the graph to explain why the processes of nuclear fission and nuclear fusion result in a release of energy.

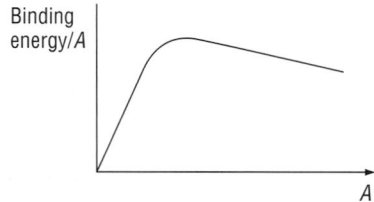

11 The core of a nuclear reactor contains fuel rods, moderator, control rods and coolant.

(a) Draw a diagram to show how these may be arranged in the core of the reactor.

(b) Describe briefly the role of each.

12 (a) A radioactive nuclide of potassium is represented by the symbol $^{42}_{19}$K. In the nucleus of such an atom, how many protons are there, and how many neutrons?

(b) This nuclide decays by beta decay to an isotope of calcium (Ca). Write an equation to represent this decay.

(c) The half-life of this isotope of potassium is 12.5 h. Use the relationship $\lambda t_{1/2} = 0.693$ to calculate its decay constant.

13 A sample of a radioactive substance has an initial activity of 50 Bq. Its decay constant is 3×10^{-3} s^{-1}.

(a) Write an equation of the form $x = x_0 e^{-\lambda t}$ to represent how the activity of the sample will change with time.

(b) What will the sample's activity be after 500 s?

(c) A Geiger counter is held near the sample. The count rate detected by the counter is less than the sample's activity. State *two* factors that contribute to this.

Module 4: Medical imaging

14 Technetium-99m ($^{99m}_{43}$Tc) has a half-life of 6 h and decays by gamma emission only. It is used as a tracer in medicine.

   (a) **(i)** Explain what is meant by *half-life*.

       (ii) State what happens to the nucleon and proton numbers when a $^{99m}_{43}$Tc nucleus emits a gamma photon.

   (b) A patient is to be injected with a dose of technetium-99m.

       (i) Why is a gamma emitter preferred to an alpha or beta emitter?

       (ii) State one advantage and one disadvantage of using an isotope with a half-life of 6 h over one with a much shorter half-life.

   (c) When the patient is injected, the activity of the technetium-99m is 2.9×10^8 Bq. Determine the activity 24 h later, assuming all the technetium-99m remains in the body.

15 In ultrasound scanning, ultrasound waves are sent into a patient's body and reflected waves are detected. The intensity I_r of a reflected wave is given by:

$$\frac{I_r}{I_0} = \frac{(Z_2 - Z_1)^2}{(Z_2 + Z_1)^2}$$

   (a) State the meanings of the terms in this equation.

   (b) A sound wave of intensity 4.0×10^{-9} W m^{-2} travels through medium 1 ($Z_1 = 400\,000$ kg m^{-2} s^{-1}). It strikes a boundary with medium 2 ($Z_2 = 480\,000$ kg m^{-2} s^{-1}). Calculate the intensity of the reflected wave.

   (c) Explain why a gel is required between the ultrasound transducer and the patient's skin during an ultrasound scan.

16 In medical diagnosis, it is desirable to use *non-invasive methods* of diagnosis. MRI is an example of a non-invasive technique.

   (a) Explain why non-invasive techniques are desirable.

   (b) Explain why MRI is described as non-invasive.

   (c) State *two* advantages MRI scanning has over X-ray scanning, and one disadvantage.

Module 5: Modelling the universe

17 **(a)** Astronomical distances may be measured in astronomical units (AU), parsecs (pc) and light-years (ly). Explain how each of these units is defined.

   (b) Give approximate values in metres for the parsec and the light-year, and hence show that 1 pc is ~3 ly.

18 Edwin Hubble discovered that the universe is apparently expanding.

   (a) What observations did he make which showed this to be the case?

   (b) State Hubble's law.

   (c) The value of the Hubble constant H_0 is approximately 70 km s^{-1} Mpc^{-1}. What is this in s^{-1}, and what does this suggest is the approximate age of the universe?

19 **(a)** Define the term *critical density*.

   (b) What do observations suggest is the value of the average density of the universe? What is the implication of this?

Appendix 1 – Accuracy and uncertainty

Physicists try to make their observations as accurate as possible. Uncertainty and errors in measurements arise in a number of ways and, as an experimentalist, you should try to minimise them.

Systematic uncertainties

These can arise in a number of ways:

- **Zero error:** e.g. an ammeter does not read zero when no current is flowing through it. If it reads +0.05 A, all of its readings will be too high. Either correct the meter to read zero, or adjust all readings to take account of the error.

- **Incorrect calibration** of an instrument: e.g. an ammeter that reads zero when no current flows, but all other readings are consistently too low or too high. It may read 9.9 A when 10.0 A is flowing. Again, either correct the meter, or adjust all readings.

- **Incorrect use** of an instrument: e.g. screwing a micrometer too tightly, or viewing a meniscus from an angle. Learn the correct technique for using instruments and apparatus.

- **Human reaction:** e.g. when starting and stopping a stopclock. You always press the button a fraction of a second after the event.

Systematic uncertainties can be reduced or even eliminated. This increases the accuracy of the final result.

Random uncertainties

These often arise as a result of judgements made by the experimenter:

- **Reading from a scale.** You may have to judge where a meter needle is on a scale – what is the nearest scale mark? What fraction of a division is nearest to the needle?

- **Timing a moving object.** When did it start to move? When did it pass the finishing line? You have to judge.

The conditions under which the measurement is made can vary:

- **Equipment** can vary. One trolley may have more friction than another. Two apparently identical resistors may have slightly different values.

- **Samples of materials** may be different. Two lengths of wire from the same reel may have slightly different compositions.

- **Conditions** can vary. Room temperature may change and affect your results.

Some measurements are intrinsically random:

- **Radioactive decay.** If you measure the background radiation in the laboratory for 30 s, you are likely to find slightly different values each time.

Random uncertainties can be reduced, but it is usually impossible to eliminate them entirely. Reducing uncertainties increases the precision of the final result.

Reducing random uncertainties

Here are some ways to reduce random uncertainties.

- **Make multiple measurements**, and find the mean (average). Roughly speaking, taking four measurements reduces the uncertainty by half; 100 measurements will divide the uncertainty by 10.
- **Plot a graph**, and draw a smooth curve or a straight line through the points.
- **Choose a suitable instrument** to reduce errors of judgement, e.g. using light gates and an electronic timer instead of timing with a stopwatch. You need to think critically about the instrument: does it introduce other sources of uncertainty?

Expressing uncertainties

Here are two ways in which the uncertainty in a final result can be expressed.

- **Use significant figures:** a calculation may give $R = 127\ \Omega$. If the uncertainty is small, you may wish to quote this as $130\ \Omega$; if the uncertainty is large, as $100\ \Omega$.
- **Use ± uncertainty:** by considering the uncertainties in individual measurements, you may be able to show the degree of uncertainty in the above result. Small uncertainty: $R = (127 \pm 2)\ \Omega$; larger uncertainty: $R = (130 \pm 10)\ \Omega$.

Summary

- Think critically about the equipment and methods you use.
- Reduce random uncertainties to increase the precision of your results.
- Reduce systematic uncertainties to increase the accuracy of your results.
- Indicate the extent of uncertainty in individual results, and in the final result.

Appendix 2 – SI units

The SI system of units is based on seven **fundamental** or **base units**. They are listed in **Table 1** below, together with the quantity of which each is the unit.

Most quantities are expressed in **derived units.** For example, area is given in m^2, acceleration in m s^{-2}. Some derived units are given special names, such as hertz or pascal. Some of these are listed in **Table 2** opposite.

It is often useful to be able to express these derived units in terms of other units. This is shown in the fourth column of the table. The fifth column shows the formulae that relate the corresponding quantities.

Sometimes it is easier to remember the relationship between units, e.g. one volt is one joule per coulomb. At other times it is easier to remember the relationship between quantities, e.g. $F = BIl$. It is a great help if you can translate between quantities and units. Then you need only remember half as many formulae.

Table 3 lists the commonly used **prefixes**, e.g. 1 μF = 1 microfarad = 10^{-6} F.

Table 1 Fundamental SI units

Quantity	Unit	Abbreviation
mass	kilogram	kg
length	metre	m
time	second	s
temperature	kelvin	K
current	ampere	A
amount of substance	mole	mol
luminous intensity	candela	cd

Table 2 Derived SI units

Quantity	Unit	Abbreviation	In terms of other units	Equation
frequency	hertz	Hz	s^{-1}	$f = 1/T$
force	newton	N	$kg\ m\ s^{-2}$	$F = ma$
energy, work	joule	J	N m	$W = Fd$
power	watt	W	$J\ s^{-1}$	$P = W/t$
charge	coulomb	C	A s	$Q = It$
p.d., e.m.f.	volt	V	$J\ C^{-1}$	$W = QV$
resistance	ohm	Ω	$V\ A^{-1}$	$V = IR$
capacitance	farad	F	$C\ V^{-1}$	$Q = CV$
magnetic flux density	tesla	T	$N\ A^{-1}\ m^{-1}$; $Wb\ m^{-2}$	$F = BIL$; $\phi = AB$
magnetic flux	weber	Wb	V s	$E = d\phi/dt$
Celsius temperature	degree Celsius	°C	K	$T = \theta + 273$
activity	becquerel	Bq	s^{-1}	$A = dN/dt$

Table 3 Prefixes

Factor	Prefix	Symbol
10^9	giga-	G
10^6	mega-	M
10^3	kilo-	k
10^{-1}	deci-	d
10^{-2}	centi-	c
10^{-3}	milli-	m
10^{-6}	micro-	μ
10^{-9}	nano-	n
10^{-12}	pico-	p
10^{-15}	femto-	f

Appendix 3 – Data and formulae for question papers

In examination papers, you will be supplied with a long list of data, formulae and relationships relevant to each unit. **Part 1** below shows the data and equations relevant to Units 1 and 2 of your A2 course.

Part 2 shows the formulae and relationships relevant to Units 1 and 2. Note that you need to be familiar with the symbols used in these equations. You should also know the circumstances in which they can be applied.

Part 3 shows the formulae and relationships relevant to AS Units 1 and 2. Some questions at A2 have a synoptic element; that is, they draw on material from the AS course.

Part 1: Data and equations supplied in question papers

speed of light in a vacuum	c	3.00×10^8 m s^{-1}
permittivity of free space	ε_0	8.85×10^{-12} C^2 N^{-1} m^{-2} (F m^{-1})
elementary charge	e	1.60×10^{-19} C
Planck constant	h	6.63×10^{-34} J s
gravitational constant	G	6.67×10^{-11} N m^2 kg^{-2}
Avogadro constant	N_A	6.02×10^{23} mol^{-1}
molar gas constant	R	8.31 J mol^{-1} K^{-1}
Boltzmann constant	k	1.38×10^{-23} J K^{-1}
electron rest mass	m_e	9.11×10^{-31} kg
proton rest mass	m_p	1.673×10^{-27} kg
neutron rest mass	m_n	1.675×10^{-27} kg
alpha particle rest mass	m_α	6.646×10^{-27} kg
acceleration of free fall	g	9.81 m s^{-2}

arc length $= r\theta$

circumference of circle $= 2\pi r$

area of circle $= \pi r^2$

curved surface area of cylinder $= 2\pi rh$

volume of cylinder $= \pi r^2 h$

area of circle $= 4\pi r^2$

volume of sphere $= \dfrac{4}{3}\pi r^3$

Pythagoras' theorem: $a^2 = b^2 + c^2$

For small angle $\theta \Rightarrow \sin\theta \approx \tan\theta \approx \theta$ and $\cos\theta \approx 1$

$\lg(AB) = \lg(A) + \lg(B)$

$$\lg\left(\frac{A}{B}\right) = \lg(A) - \lg(B)$$

$$\ln(x^n) = n\ln(x)$$

$$\ln(e^{kx}) = kx$$

Hint

Note that, although these formulae are supplied in question papers, you still need to understand them and know when they can be applied.

Part 2: Formulae and relationships supplied in question papers

Unit 1 – Newtonian world

$$F = \frac{\Delta p}{\Delta t}$$

$$v = \frac{2\pi r}{T}$$

$$a = \frac{v^2}{r}$$

$$F = \frac{mv^2}{r}$$

$$F = \frac{GMm}{r^2}$$

$$g = \frac{F}{m}$$

$$g = \frac{GM}{r^2}$$

$$T^2 = \left(\frac{4\pi^2}{GM}\right)r^3$$

$$f = \frac{1}{T}$$

$$\omega = \frac{2\pi}{T} = 2\pi f$$

$$a = -(2\pi f)^2 x$$

$$x = A\cos(2\pi ft)x$$

$$v_{max} = (2\pi f)A$$

$$E = mc\Delta\theta$$

$$pV = NkT$$

$$pV = nRT$$

$$E = \frac{3}{2}kT$$

Unit 2 – Fields, particles and frontiers of physics

$$E = \frac{F}{Q}$$

$$F = \frac{Qq}{4\pi\varepsilon_0 r^2}$$

$$E = \frac{Q}{4\pi\varepsilon_0 r^2}$$

$$F = \frac{V}{d}$$

$$F = BIL\sin\theta$$

$$F - BQv$$

$$\phi = BA\cos\theta$$

induced e.m.f. = – rate of change of magnetic flux linkage

$$\frac{V_s}{V_p} = \frac{n_s}{n_p}$$

$$Q = VC$$

$$W = \frac{1}{2}QV \qquad W = \frac{1}{2}CV^2$$

time constant $= CR$

$$x = x_0 e^{-\frac{t}{CR}}$$

$$C = C_1 + C_2 + C_3$$

$$\frac{1}{C} = \frac{1}{C_1} + \frac{1}{C_2} + \frac{1}{C_3}$$

$$A = \lambda N$$

$$A = A_0 e^{-\lambda t}$$

$$N = N_0 e^{-\lambda t}$$

$$\lambda t_{1/2} = 0.693$$

$$\Delta E = \Delta mc^2$$

$$I = I_0 e^{-\mu x}$$

$$Z = \rho c$$

$$\frac{I_r}{I_0} = \frac{(Z_2 - Z_1)^2}{(Z_2 - Z_1)^2}$$

$$\frac{\Delta\lambda}{\lambda} \approx \frac{v}{c}$$

age of universe $\approx \dfrac{1}{H_0}$

$$\rho_0 = \frac{3H_0^2}{8\pi G}$$

Examiner tip

Test yourself: read through the list of formulae before taking a test, and ensure that you know what all the symbols represent and when each formula can be used.

Part 3: Formulae and relationships from the AS course

Unit 1: Mechanics

$F_x = F \cos \theta$

$F_y = F \sin \theta$

$a = \dfrac{\Delta v}{\Delta t}$

$v = u + at$

$s = \frac{1}{2}(u + v)t$

$s = ut + \frac{1}{2} at^2$

$s = vt - \frac{1}{2} at^2$

$v^2 = u^2 + 2as$

$F = ma$

$W = mg$

$\text{moment} = Fx$

$\text{torque} = Fd$

$\rho = M/V$

$p = F/A$

$W = Fx \cos \theta$

$E_k = \frac{1}{2} mv^2$

$E_p = mgh$

$\text{efficiency} = \dfrac{\text{useful energy output}}{\text{total energy input}} \times 100\%$

$F = kx$

$E = \frac{1}{2} Fx = \frac{1}{2} kx^2$

$\text{stress} = \dfrac{F}{A}$

$\text{strain} = \dfrac{x}{L}$

$\text{Young modulus} = \dfrac{\text{stress}}{\text{strain}}$

Unit 2: Electrons, waves and photons

$\Delta Q = I \Delta t$

$I = Anev$

$W = VQ$

$V = IR$

$R = R_1 + R_2 + R_3 + \ldots \text{ in series}$

$\dfrac{1}{R} = \dfrac{1}{R_1} + \dfrac{1}{R_2} + \dfrac{1}{R_3} + \ldots \text{ in parallel}$

$R = \dfrac{\rho l}{A}$

$P = VI = I^2 R = \dfrac{V^2}{R}$

$W = VIt$

$\text{e.m.f.} = V + Ir$

$V_{out} = \dfrac{R_2}{R_1 + R_2} \times V_{in}$

$v = f\lambda$

$\lambda = \dfrac{ax}{D}$

$d \sin \theta = n\lambda$

$E = hf = \dfrac{hc}{\lambda}$

$hf = \phi + KE_{max}$

$\lambda = \dfrac{h}{mv}$

Appendix 4 – Electrical circuit symbols

You need to be able to recall and use appropriate circuit symbols; you also need to be able to draw and interpret circuit diagrams that include these symbols.

Name of device	Symbol
Junction of conductors (optional dot)	
Conductors crossing (no connection)	
Cell	
Battery of cells	
Open terminals	
Indicator or light source	
Fixed resistor	
Potentiometer (voltage divider)	
Light-dependent resistor (LDR)	
Thermistor	
Ammeter	
Voltmeter	
Semiconductor diode	
Light-emitting diode (LED)	
Switch	

Answers to quick check questions

Unit 1 – The Newtonian world

Module 1 – Newton's laws and momentum

Momentum
1. mass, kinetic energy
2. 1.5×10^6 kg m s^{-1} due west
3. Small mass × great velocity = greater mass × smaller velocity.
4. 22 500 kg m s^{-1}
5. Boy has more momentum, girl has more kinetic energy.
6. The time for which the force acts.
7. 300 N
8. 1 kg m s^{-1}; 2.96 kg m s^{-1}; 3.92 N

Collisions and explosions
1. 10 m s^{-1}
2. 2 m s^{-1} to right
3. 15 m s^{-1}

Newton's laws of motion
1. zero; constant
2. 50 kN; GPE increases
3. two contact forces; two forces on person
4. 3000 N s; 3000 kg m s^{-1}
5. 6.0 N

Module 2 – Circular motion and oscillations

Describing circular motion
1. 2π; π; $\pi/2$ or 1.57; $\pi/3$ or 1.05; $\pi/4$ or 0.79
2. 57.3°; 14.3°; 180°; 360°; 36°
3. 120°
4. 524 s; 44 s
5. Velocity, acceleration and force are all changing (vectors).

Centripetal force and acceleration
1. friction with road (and contact force of road, if not horizontal)
2. 31.6 N
3. smaller r so larger F
4. 12.5 m s^{-2}
5. 1700 m s^{-1}

Gravitational fields
1. uniform field – parallel field lines; slight separation of field lines; greater separation
2. 8 N; 0.8 m
3. 533 N

Orbiting under gravity
1. Orbital period of Mars is longer than Earth's; its orbital speed is less.
2. (a) 2.36×10^6 s
   (b) 3.83×10^6 m
3. 7600 m s^{-1}; 5800 s
4. 4.5×10^5 m

Simple harmonic motion
1. 5 cm; 5.0 s; 0.2 Hz; 1.26 rad s^{-1}
2. 0.87 s; 1.15 Hz; 7.2 rad s^{-1}
3. 40π rad s^{-1}; 20 Hz; 0.05s

4. at midpoint; at ends of oscillation
5. 0.44 m s^{-1}

More about SHM
1. see graphs on page 18
2. 4 cm; 0.095 Hz; −3.96 cm
3. $x = 0.2 \sin(\pi t)$; 0.118 m
4. KE
5. decreases

Module 3 – Thermal physics

Solid, liquid and gas
1. both: gas
2. 400 kPa (= 4×10^5 Pa)
3. Each has half.
4. only heating
5. A: solid; B: solid + liquid; C: liquid; D: liquid + gas; E: gas. Internal energy increasing in all.

Temperature
1. (a) A and D
   (b) from D to C
2. Thermal energy will flow from X to Y.
3. Internal energy is at its lowest value at this temperature.
4. 273 K, 223 K
5. −273 °C, −173 °C, 27 °C, 100 °C
6. 145 K

Specific heat capacity
1. B
2. 18 000 J
3. 45.5 °C
4. 500 J kg^{-1} K^{-1}
5. Description of experiment – see page 25

How gases behave
1. Volume is halved, provided mass and temperature unchanged.
2. 160 l
3. 180 kPa
4. Pressure doubles.
5. 178 kPa
6. During collisions between molecules, no kinetic energy is lost (kinetic energy is conserved).

Ideal gases
1. 3.01×10^{24} particles in each
2. 241 K (−32 °C)
3. 4 litres
4. 9.7×10^{-3} m^3
5. Average kinetic energy doubles; stays the same.
6. 5.2×10^{-21} J

Unit 2 – Fields, particles and frontiers of physics

Module 1 – Electric and magnetic fields

Electric fields
1. parallel, equally spaced lines
2. 1.6×10^{-15} N
3. 300 V m^{-1} (or 300 N C^{-1})
4. $E \propto V$; $E \propto 1/d$

5 1.92 N

6 The resultant force on the particle is upwards, so it will accelerate upwards.

Coulomb's law

1 equal and opposite repulsive forces

2 230 N

3 1×10^{11} N C^{-1}

Magnetic fields and forces

1 field lines similar to bar magnet; greater current: more lines and closer together

2 0.66 N; down into paper

3 1.6×10^{-13} N

4 up out of paper

5 0.57 mm

6 the faster; the faster

Electromagnetic induction

1 0.2 T

2 0.079 Wb

3 the first two

4 towards A; positive

5 1 : 20; 240 V

Module 2 – Capacitors and exponential decay

Capacitors

1 8 μF; 160 μC

2 5

3 40 μF

4 2 μF; 40 mJ

Discharging a capacitor

1 Graph A – bigger R, so takes longer.

2 22.3 V

3 240 μA; 32.5 μA

4 both the same

Module 3 – Nuclear physics

Atomic structure

1 Thicker foil means more chance of 'direct hit', so more back-scattered.

2 5 orders (10^5)

3 10^4

4 $^{28}_{14}$Si

5 8 of each

6 A and D; B and C (same proton numbers)

Nuclear processes and forces

1 $^{210}_{84}$Po $\rightarrow$ $^{206}_{82}$Pb + $^{4}_{2}$He + γ; $^{42}_{19}$K $\rightarrow$ $^{42}_{20}$Ca + $^{0}_{-1}$e + γ + $\bar{\nu}$

2 proton = uud so charge = +2/3e + 2/3e − 1/3e = e; neutron = udd so charge = +2/3e − 1/3e − 1/3e = 0

3 for both: $B = 1$, $S = 0$

4 electron (= beta-minus); antineutrino; gamma photon

Mass – energy conservation

1 Mass of neutron > mass of proton + electron; more mass–energy is needed.

2 4.4×10^9 kg s^{-1}

3 Mass of products < mass of mother.

4 2

5 a proton ($^{1}_{1}$H)

6 Slow down: lower rods further into reactor; this absorbs neutrons so fewer go on to cause further fissions. Speed up: raise rods so that fewer neutrons are absorbed.

Radioactive decay

1 γ

2 200 Bq

3 Background count not excluded; not all decays detected.

4 625 Bq

5 1.2×10^{-6} s^{-1}

6 70 000

Radioactive decay equations

1 $A \propto N$, so A decreases as N decreases.

2 $C = C_0 e^{-\lambda t}$

3 34.4 Bq

4 1.23×10^{-4} yr^{-1}

5 115.5 s; 0.30

6 0.99 after 100 y; 4.6×10^{-6} after 100 000 y; the first is too small a change to be measured, the last is too small a fraction remaining to be measurable.

Module 4 – Medical imaging

X-rays

1 (Electrical) energy supplied by power supply to electron beam becomes energy of X-rays (a small fraction) + heat carried away by cooling system.

2 Highest energy of X-rays increases; overall intensity increases; characteristic X-rays appear.

3 **(a)** Overall brightness will increase as more X-rays reach the detector.

   (b) An image with high contrast has a big difference in intensity between bright and dark areas.

4 W m^{-2}

5 0.25 transmitted (0.75 absorbed)

6 Intestine is surrounded by other soft tissue, so little difference in absorption (low contrast).

Diagnostic methods in medicine

1 **(a)** Shorter – would decay before reaching patient; longer – would remain radioactive in patient long after diagnosis, and would decay more slowly so that bigger dose would be needed.

   (b) Gammas needed because they can penetrate the body and be detected outside.

2 Site is closer to first detector.

3 **(a)** increases

   (b) frequency of RF waves matches natural frequency of nuclei

4 **(a)** large electromagnet

   (b) provide steadily increasing field across patient

   (c) one transmits, the other detects

5 CAT scan uses X-rays, good for detecting bones; MRI better for seeing damage to soft tissue.

Ultrasound in medicine

1 Produce: varying voltage produces stress which causes crystal to change dimensions. Detect: ultrasound produces varying stress in crystal which produces varying voltage.

2 3.64×10^6 kg m^{-2} s^{-1}

3 0.58

4 4.4×10^{-3}

5 The beating heart changes shape during the scan so an unclear image results.

6 The frequency of the reflected ultrasound waves would change.

Module 5 – Modelling the universe

The structure of the universe

1 **(a)** gravity

   (b) interstellar cloud of dust and gas

   (c) GPE transformed to thermal energy

Answers to quick check questions

2 **(a)** star – red giant – white dwarf
   (b) star – super red giant – supernova – neutron star or black hole
3 9.3×10^{12} km
4 **(a)** Star B
   (b) 0.01 pc
5 We must assume that the parts of the universe which we can observe are typical, or we will be unable to deduce anything about the universe in general.

The expanding universe
1 It is moving towards us (or it has a component of velocity towards us).
2 3.7×10^7 m s^{-1}
3 125 nm $(= 1.25 \times 10^{-7}$ m)
4 Graph would curve over to lower values at greater distances.

5 **(a)** younger (because, if moving faster, will have taken less time to expand)
   (b) 12.4×10^9 y

The evolution of the universe
1 **(a)** Temperature will decrease as energy spread over greater volume.
   (b) Wavelengths will get longer (waves stretched out; less energy corresponds to lower frequency or higher wavelength).
2 quarks, leptons, photons
3 protons   atomic nuclei   neutral atoms   stars
4 The mass of all the matter in the universe
5 less
6 **(a)** It will expand for ever, never contract.
   (b) It will slow down, stop, contract to big crunch.

Answers to end-of-unit questions

Unit 1 – The Newtonian world

1 (a) product of mass and velocity; a vector quantity
 (b) 1.2×10^5 kg m s^{-1}
 (c) When two or more objects interact, their total momentum remains constant provided no external force acts (i.e. within a closed system).
 (d) (i) The child gains upward momentum, the Earth gains downward momentum.
  (ii) The child's momentum is transferred to the Earth.
2 (a) Total KE remains constant.
 (b) (i) mv before = 0.005×1 kg m s^{-1}
     = mv after.
  (ii) KE before = × 0.005 kg × (1 m s^{-1})^2 = KE after.
3 480 m s^{-1} in opposite direction to cannon
4 (a) 1.2 m s^{-1}
 (b) KE before = 4.41 J; KE after = 2.52 J; not conserved
 (c) inelastic
5 (a) 60 N s
 (b) 60 N s (or 60 kg m s^{-1})
 (c) 1.25 m s^{-1}
6 (a) A: 6 m s^{-1}, B: 10 m s^{-1}.
 (b) 8 m s^{-1}
7 (a) The combined momentum of the two marbles is zero. They will rebound with their initial velocities exactly reversed.
 (b) They will rebound with equal but opposite velocities. Their velocities will be less than v, and could be zero.
8 (a) In diagram: v is tangential, F is radial.
 (b) $F = mv^2/r$
9 (a) 0.042 m s^{-1}
 (b) 0.31 rad s^{-1}
10 (a) $F = GMm/r^2$; the two forces are equal and opposite (and in same straight line)
 (b) 13.5 km s^{-1}
 (c) 3.3×10^5 s
11 (a) An orbit above the Earth's equator with period of orbit equal to Earth's rotational period.
 (b) Above the equator, in same direction as Earth's rotation, with period = 24 h.
 (c) TV broadcasting; telecommunications relays
12 (a) SHM: the acceleration of a mass is directed towards a fixed point and is proportional to its displacement from that point.
 (b) 5 cm; 0.4 s; 2.5 Hz
 (c & d) x/cm

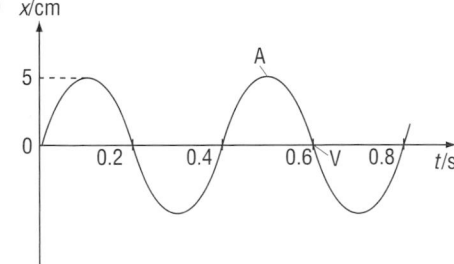

 (e) $x = 0.05 \sin(5\pi t)$; 0
 (f) 12.3 m s^{-2}; at maximum displacement

13 (a) 0.0025 Hz
 (b) $a = -2.47\, x$
 (c) When displacement = ± amplitude
 (d) 0.25 m s^{-2}
14 (a) Resonance happens when forcing frequency = natural frequency, and maximum amplitude vibrations occur.
 (b)

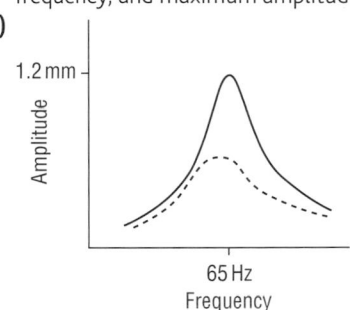

 (c) friction introduced to reduce amplitude
 (d) See dotted line in **b**.
15 90.9×10^6 m; 13 200 m s^{-1}
16 If the rod, area A, is displaced downwards through distance x; volume of water displaced = Ax. Weight of water displaced = $AxDg$, where D = density of water. This is the restoring force F. So $F = -AxDg$, and we have $F \propto x$, the condition for SHM.
17 (a) A, B, C: internal energy increasing
 (b) A: KE increasing; B: PE increasing; C: KE increasing
 (c) 60 kJ kg^{-1}
 (d) Energy required to melt a substance at constant temperature
18 See description on page 25.
19 (a) The internal energy of a system is the sum of a random distribution of kinetic and potential energies associated with the particles of the system.
 (b) (i) 0 K
  (ii) −273.15 °C
20 (a) The volume of a fixed mass of gas is proportional to its pressure, provided the temperature remains constant.
 (b) 225 kPa
21 (a) the amount of a substance
 (b) $pV = RT$ (because $n = 1$)
 (c) 124 kPa
22 (a) N = number of molecules
 (b) 6.2×10^{-21} J
23 1.36
24 Both types of molecule have the same mean KE (= 3/2 kT). CO_2 molecules have greater mass. Since KE = ½ mv^2, it follows that they have a slower mean speed.

Indicates Stretch and Challenge answer

Unit 2 – Fields, particles and the frontiers of physics

1 (a) direction of field: direction of field line at a point; magnitude: lines closer together = stronger field.

(b) magnitudes: equal; directions: opposite (Newton's third law)

2 (a)

(b) 20 kV m^{-1}

(c) 2×10^{-11} N

(d) Force is unchanged.

3 (a) (i) 500×10^3 V m^{-1}

(ii) 5.0×10^{-11} N

(iii) 125 m s^{-2}

(b) downward force on dust particle

(c) constant acceleration downwards, constant velocity horizontally, therefore path is parabolic

4 (a)

(b) 0.2 T

(c) 0.03 N

5 (a) 3×10^{-4} Wb; 3×10^{-2} Wb

(b) Flux linking coil is not changing.

(c) Rotate it, or move it out of field.

6 (a) 4 mC (4×10^{-3} C)

(b) 0.8 J

(c) parallel; 20 μF

(d) 200 V

(e) 0.2 J; one quarter

7 (a) 200 μA (2×10^{-4} A)

(b) I/mA

(c) 1000 s

(d) $I = 2 \times 10^{-4}$ exp($-t$/1000)

(e) 120 μA (1.2×10^{-4} A)

8 (a) 2.5 V

(b) slope = 10 μC/18 s = 0.56 μA

(c) $R = V/I = 2.5/0.5 \times 10^{-6} = 4.5$ MΩ

9 (a) Alpha particles are easily absorbed by air.

(b) Most alpha particles deflected only slightly; a small fraction back-scattered towards source.

(c) Back-scattering suggested something with high positive charge and large mass but small volume off which the alpha particles were scattering.

(d) Alpha particles

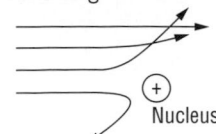

Nucleus

10 In fission, a nucleus with large A splits to form two nuclei with smaller A. Total number of nucleons is unchanged. On the graph, fission is represented by movement to left from right-hand end. Binding energy per nucleon increases; energy is released in the process.

11 (a) See diagram on page 53.

(b) Fuel rods: contain fissile fuel; release heat when chain reaction established.
Moderator: slows down neutrons to thermal speeds so that they interact more strongly with fissile nuclei
control rods: absorb neutrons to slow down reaction
coolant: transports heat away from reactor core to boiler.

12 (a) 19 protons, 23 neutrons

(b) $^{42}_{19}$K $\rightarrow$ $^{42}_{20}$Ca + $^{0}_{-1}$e + energy

(c) $\lambda = 0.055$ h^{-1}

13 (a) $A = 50$ exp($-3 \times 10^{-3}t$)

(b) 11 Bq

(c) Not all particles emitted reach Geiger tube; some pass straight through the tube.

14 (a) (i) time for activity to fall to half initial value

(ii) A and Z remain unchanged

(b) (i) less risk of internal cell damage, since γ less ionising

(ii) advantage: 6 h long enough for imaging to take place; disadvantage: greater exposure risk

(c) 1.8×10^7 Bq

15 (a) I_0 = intensity of incident ultrasound; Z_1 and Z_2 are acoustic impedances of materials 1 and 2.

(b) 3.6×10^{-9} W m^{-2}

(c) If air comes between scanner and skin, most ultrasound is reflected and so does not penetrate the patient. This is because air and skin have very different values of acoustic impedance Z.

16 (a) Invasive techniques can expose the patient to infection, can be painful, take time to heal.

(b) The patient's skin does not have to be cut; no tools or equipment are put into body.

(c) In MRI, radiation is non-ionising; different soft tissues can be distinguished. However, bone is not clearly shown.

17 (a) AU: average distance of Earth from Sun; 1 pc = distance to star whose parallax is 2 seconds of arc; 1 light-year = distance travelled by light through free space in 1 year.

(b) 1 pc ~ 3×10^{16} m; 1 ly ~ 9×10^{15} m;
1 pc = 3×10^{16}/9×10^{15} ~ 3.26

18 (a) Redshifts showed that distant galaxies were receding from Earth.

(b) Velocity of recession ∝ distance to galaxy

(c) 70 km s^{-1} Mpc^{-1} = 70 000/3×10^{22} = 2.3×10^{-18} s^{-1}; age of universe = 4.3×10^{17} s

19 (a) The average density of the universe such that, at any greater density, the universe will eventually start to contract under its own gravity.

(b) Average density is close to critical density; the universe may be 'flat'.

Indicates Stretch and Challenge answer

Index